BEGINNER + INTERMEDIATE + ADVANCED GUIDE TO BLADESMITHING

WES SANDER

TABLE OF CONTENTS

BLADESMITHING FOR BEGINNERS

MAKE YOUR FIRST KNIFE IN 7 STEPS

WES SANDER

INTRODUCTION

One of the earliest knives made from smelted metal was discovered in a tomb in Anatolia. It was dated to the year 2,500 BC. However, iron was not included as a vital material in the making of knives until the year 500 BC.

Since then, the metal took new importance in crafting of various tools and implements. Greeks, Celts, Egyptians, and Vikings began to use iron into their metalworks. It was not until the development and discovery of steel that metalwork took on a whole new form.

We have come a long way since the first time man discovered the use of iron. Back then, the tools and knives that were produced were crude implements. They were there to serve a necessity and made using simple techniques.

Today, knife making is a process. It starts with finding the right steel, forging the knife, then subjecting the tool to an annealing and normalizing process. It is then shaped with grinding, heat treated, quenched, and finally tempered.

While our ancestors may not have been particularly careful about their working conditions, we should always make sure that we protect ourselves.

- Implement the use of safety glasses to protect our eyes from unwanted materials - such as hot metal and sharp debris - from flying into our eyes.
- Hearing protection is vital since prolonged exposure to loud sounds (for example, the noise of metal grinding) can affect hearing.
- Use a respirator to protect from tiny dust and other particles that can enter the lungs and cause permanent damage.
- Do not wear shorts, even on hot days. Hot sparks can fly off the metal and burn the skin.
- Put on leather bibs so that any stray spark hits a layer of fireproof material rather than your clothes.
- Tie up long hair when working with tools and metals. Make sure to secure a longer beard or keep them away using other means during metalworking.
- Since you are just starting, get comfortable using gloves. Eventually, they can become optional as you gain experience working with metals. But for now, better to err on the side of caution. Note: Do not use gloves while using any sort of spinning tool like a buffer or grinder. They could get caught in the mechanism.

Most importantly, have fun in the process. Don't be afraid to experiment. After all, it is only through experimentation that you can find out what you should do and what you are not supposed to do. Familiarize yourself with the basics and put the things you learn into practice.

Mistakes happen. That's alright. You may find out that your knives break, or you have an oddly shaped knife in your hands. Remember, there are only two things that are going to happen during knife making:

- You make a knife, whether it is perfect or not.

- You learn a lesson.

The lessons you learn are one of the most important aspects of knife making. You go from making regular knives to creating something like the one below.

Figure 1: Knife with tasteful curves.

So do not easily despair when you are working on your knife. Keep your focus on what you want to achieve, and you will get there eventually.

Take your time to understand the steps and information provided in this book. Make sure you know what you are working with and keep trying until you perfect it.

Design, Stock removal, grinding bevels, heat treatment, adding the handle, polishing, sharpening – these are the 7 steps with which you will make your first knife. But it's not the what, but the how to that will make you learn this craft.

With that, let's dive deeper into the art of bladesmithing.

FREE BONUSES FOR THE READERS

First of all, I want to congratulate you on taking the right steps to learn and improve your bladesmithing skills, by buying this book.

Few people take action on improving their craft, and you are one of them.

This book has exhaustive knowledge on bladesmithing and will help you make your first knife.

However, to get the most out of this book, I have 3 resources for you that will REALLY kickstart your knife making process and improve the quality of your knives.

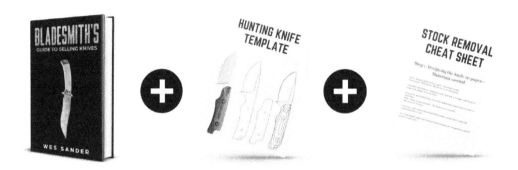

Since you are now a reader of my books, I want to extend a hand, and improve our author-reader relationship, by offering you all 3 of these bonuses for FREE.

All you have to do is go to **http://www.elitebladesmithingmasterclass.com/free-bonus** and enter the e-mail where you want to receive these resources.

These bonuses will help you:

1. Make more money when selling your knives to customers
2. Save time while knife making

Here's what you receive for FREE:

1. Bladesmith's Guide to Selling Knives
2. Hunting Knife Template
3. Stock Removal Cheat Sheet

Here is a brief description of what you will receive in your inbox:

1. Bladesmith's Guide to Selling Knives

Do you want to sell your knives to support your hobby, but don't know where to start?

Are you afraid to charge more for your knives?

Do you constantly get low-balled on the price of your knives?

'Bladesmith's Guide to Selling Knives' contains simple but fundamental secrets to selling your knives for profit.

Both audio and PDF versions are included.

Inside this book you will discover:

- How to **make more money** when selling knives and swords to customers (Higher prices)
- The **hidden-in-plain-sight** location that is perfect for selling knives (Gun shows)
- Your **biggest 'asset'** that you can leverage to charge higher prices for your knives, and **make an extra $50 or more** off of selling the same knife.
- 4 critical mistakes you could be making, that are **holding you back from selling your knife for what it's truly worth**
- The ideal number of knives you should bring to a knife show
- 5 online platforms where you can sell your knives

- 9 key details you need to mention when selling your knives online, that will increase the customers you get

2. Hunting Knife Template for Stock Removal

Tired of drawing plans when making a knife?

Not good at CAD or any sort of design software?

Make planning and drawing layouts a 5-second affair, by downloading this classic bowie knife design that you can print and grind on your preferred size of stock steel.

Here's what you get:

- Classic bowie knife design **you can print and paste** on stock steel and start grinding
- Remove the hassle of planning and drawing the knife layout during knife making
- Detailed plans included, <u>to ensure straight and clean grind lines</u>

3. Stock Removal Cheat Sheet

Do you need to quickly lookup the correct knife making steps, while working on a knife in your workshop?

Here's what you get:

- Make your knife through stock removal in just **14 steps**
- Full stock removal process, done with 1084 steel
- **Quick reference guide** you can print and place in your workshop

As mentioned above, **to get access to this content, go to _http://www.elitebladesmithingmasterclass.com/ free-bonus_ and enter the e-mail where you want to receive these 3 resources.**

DISCLAIMER: By signing up for the free content you are also agreeing to be added to my bladesmithing e-mail list, to which I send helpful bladesmithing tips and promotional offers.

I would suggest you download these resources before you proceed further, as they are a great supplement for this book, and have the potential to bring an improvement in your results.

CHAPTER 1: TOOLS OF THE TRADE

This book has been designed to include as little filler material as possible. This allows you to jump into a process and start working on it immediately. One way to approach this book is to read a chapter then apply it in your workshop. Try practicing and understanding the techniques in each section before you move on to the next one. This will allow you to absorb the information better and memorize one technique before you begin with the next.

But before you even begin working on metals, you do need to know all the essential tools for the process.

Tools for Your Workspace

The process of knifemaking is more than just about applying skills to create something. As you continue to make progress in knifemaking, you will be using various tools to get the results that you want. You need one set of tools to get the shape of the knife and another to make its surface smooth. The following tools will act as a starting point for making your first knife based on the processes mentioned in this book. As you get familiar with the process, I encourage you to experiment and improvise with the tools to find a technique that works best for you.

Workbench

Your workbench is going to be your main space for a lot of your work. But more than that, it will act as a space to host all the vital tools you require. One of the essential things to note is that your workbench should be elevated to a comfortable height. By doing so, you won't have to bend over and strain your back muscles while working. Additionally, it's very important that your workbench be stable so that it doesn't move around when you're working on your blade. If anchoring it to the floor or wall isn't possible, try to add weight on the bottom to create a solid base with as little movement as possible.

Angle Grinder

It is not necessary to have this tool right way. However, it definitely saves time when using it for different tasks such as grinding or cutting metal. An important point to note here is that you need to be extremely cautious when handling an angle grinder.

Drill

Since you will need a tool that can easily punch holes into the knife's tang (more on this later) so that you can attach your handle, it is important to get yourself a drill press. You can also make use of a hand drill, but a drill press allows you to make accurate holes while you balance your knife carefully.

Files

While the bulk of the work is done using power tools, it is nonetheless useful to have a file around. You can accomplish specific tasks efficiently, such as quickly removing a minor metal burr or fine-tuning the knife design. When you have a file around, you can take your time to work on your knife and get the result that you want.

Belt Grinder/Belt Sander

A valuable tool to have in your work space, and as you will notice when we start working with knives, it is an essential part of the process.

You can always use the angle grinder to perform many of the tasks of a belt grinder, but I would recommend keeping the angle grinder for cutting. The belt grinder is much safer and easier to use. Plus, you can perform a plethora of tasks on it including shaping handles, grinding bevels, adding the finishing touches to your knife, and more.

One of the cheaper options for a belt grinder is the 1 x 30-inch version. The grinder itself won't be as rugged or versatile as the other varieties that you can get in the market, but it will help you out as a beginner.

The more expensive version is the 2 x 72-inch belt grinder. With the step-up in investment, you also get a hardier and sturdier grinder. This will improve the quality of the output you are producing.

Quenchant

Quenching is a vital part of the knifemaking process. For the process, you need a container called the 'quenchant.'

During the process of quenching, there is a possibility that your blade could "flare-up," or the oil could begin flaming. For such scenarios, it is always ideal to keep the container used for quenching fireproof. Additionally, you should also make sure that your quench comes with a lid so that you can quickly cut off the supply of oxygen in case of an emergency.

Many people use an improvised container as a quench. You can do the same by using a used metal coffee container. If you are using such a container, then the idea is that you are going to work with blades that can easily fit into the container.

If heat treating 1084 steel, you can use a container of canola oil for quenching.

Other items that you can use as a quench include a 5-gallon steel bucket, a loaf pan, a heavy metal roasting pan, and even a used fire extinguisher with the top part cut off (yeah, that's a thing). But no matter what container you choose, make sure that it is fireproof and has a lid. And oh yes, do not start cutting fire extinguishers without proper equipment and knowledge. It is complex, and you might injure yourself.

Hacksaw

The hacksaw works similarly to an angle grinder, but it allows you to make fine adjustments whenever you are cutting. You can stop and adjust your position much easier with the hacksaw than with the angle grinder. It also takes longer, since you are doing the cutting by hand.

Tools for Smithing

There are tools that you will need in your workplace, and there are those tools that you need to have with you in person. They all serve an important purpose, as you will notice when we are working with knives.

Here is something to remember: the number of tools that you can find in a bladesmith's workshop and various purposes that they serve can be quite overwhelming to understand. You might visit a workshop and be amazed at some of the objects you find, wondering just what they can be used for. Since you are a beginner, you don't have to worry about too many tools. You need only to have the below for now.

Hammer

A bladesmith striking iron with a hammer is, in fact, the quintessential symbolic representation of making a powerful weapon or tool.

There is a reason for that. Your hammer is going to be of the most versatile tool that you are going to use in your knife making process. Think of the hammer as an extension of your arm, reaching out to touch the metal and work with it where your hands cannot (after all, the metals are heated to high temperatures).

Hammering is all about efficiency, so take the time to make your hammer as comfortable as possible. If you have to, you can shave the handle down to fit your hand snugly. You should be able to grasp it easily without having to use a death grip. Your body will get used to working with a particular length, and it helps you become more accurate in time.

One of the most important factors you should consider when choosing a hammer is its weight. It should be light enough that you are not going to cause muscle fatigue. The head of your hammer should weigh anywhere between 1.5 to 3 pounds.

The next thing you should focus on is the length of the handle. It should ideally be the same length as the distance from your elbow to the tips of your fingers. This allows you to work with the metal without keeping close to it.

Tongs

What the movies don't show you is that many bladesmiths use their tongs. If one hand holds the hammer, the other holds the tongs, even though tongs don't usually get the coverage that they deserve.

In a knife making process, you are usually handling metals that are heated up to 1,500°F. You can't touch metals at that temperature using your gloves. You need special equipment that can hold the metal securely and comfortably.

To put it plainly, you need tongs.

Anvil

If you are planning to buy a brand-new anvil, then you might have to shell out a little cash. But usually, you will be able to find anvils for sale or being sold second hand. You can get any type of anvil, but beware of any deep chips or indentations that will cause problems when you use it in the future.

Many bladesmiths like using anvils that are at least 100 pounds, but you can use something smaller when first starting out. The one thing I would like to point out is that the lighter the anvil, the more energy it absorbs when you are working with metal. The heavier it is, the more the metal will feel the impact. This is important because you want the metal to feel the impacts rather than the anvil.

Anvil Stand

This is not vital, but it helps you keep your anvil and the metal steady when you are working. Sometimes, you might experience situations where your anvil can slide along the floor.

The most important reason for getting a stand is to elevate the anvil. Unlike how you see them in movies, the anvil is not that tall. This means you can end up leaning or bending down to work on your metal. Even if you use a chair, you might be in an awkward position to perform your metalworking process. By using a stand, you can raise the anvil for greater comfort.

Want to know the ideal height for your anvil? Place your arms by your side and make a fist. You should place your anvil at the same level as your knuckles.

Another thing that you should focus on is the positioning of your anvil. Ideally, it should be close to your forge but not too close. You should be able to transfer the metal from the forge as quickly as possible with enough room to navigate.

Figure 2: A 55-pound anvil placed on a metal bench.

Forge

You can typically find two kinds of forges, coal-based, and propane-based. Both have their own set of advantages and limitations.

Coal-Based

These forges are quieter than their propane counterparts. You can also easily get the heat centered around a particular area. This allows them to be truly versatile.

Their drawback is that they are not ideal for beginners. They require a lot of maintenance. If you are not careful or used to them, then they can easily overheat and end up ruining your work. Also, because coal is not particularly clean to handle, you might find them getting dirty quite often.

Propane-Based

The best part about propane-based forge is that they can easily be started and require less time to get used to or work with. They are quite convenient to use and have a higher degree of portability than coal-based forges.

On the flip side, they are quite noisy and require proper ventilation. You should make sure that you are not using propane-based forge inside an enclosed space or there are risks of carbon monoxide poisoning.

The Ideal Forge

If you are getting started, then you could try using a two-brick propane forge. But as mentioned above, make sure that your workspace has proper space. If you are working inside a garage, then make sure that the garage door is wide open to carry out the exhaust and smoke from the propane forge. Additionally, if you are feeling faint or uncomfortable working with a propane forge, then make sure you stop your work, find enough ventilation, move the forge to a different location, and try again.

Starting With Steel

You are going to come across various steels to work with. There are steels such as 5160, W1, W2, O1, and more. Each type of steel that you find has its own properties.

But which one should you start with? Is there a beginner steel that you can use to practice knife making? Is there a steel that does not pose too many challenges?

Fortunately, there is.

In the world of knifemaking, 1084 is considered a beginner's steel. This steel is one of the most uncomplicated steels that you can work with at home. 1084 is part of the ten series of steels. The higher the number, the higher the percentage of carbon that they have. For example, 1045 has 0.45% carbon out of the total composition of elements in the steel. Here are the remaining steel variations of the ten series:

10 Series Steel	Percentage of Carbon
1045	0.45%
1050	0.50%
1055	0.55%
1060	0.60%
1084	0.84%
1095	0.95%

As you can see from the table above, 1084 has enough carbon to give you the sturdiness that you require for your knifemaking. At the same time, it is easier to heat treat 1084. This makes it ideal for getting used to various processes.

Additionally, it takes time to work on other forms of steel. If you start off using a more challenging type of steel and you do not like the results that come out in the end, then you are going to be that much more disappointed and completely exhausted by the entire knife making process. This is why, when you start with the 1084 steel, you won't mind making mistakes.

When you master 1084, you can feel free to move on to 1095, which has a higher carbon content and requires careful attention and skill while going through heat treatment.

CHAPTER 2: ANATOMY OF A KNIFE

Before you start working on a knife, you need to know more about its anatomy. This knowledge will help you understand just what you are working with and the parts you are going to handle.

Basic Anatomy

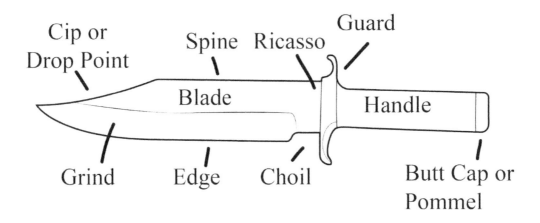

Figure 3: The anatomy of a knife

Point

The point is the tip of the knife. Or in other words, it is the business end of the knife.

Belly

The belly of the knife is the arc that is formed along the edge of the knife. It is a curved region that starts from the middle of the knife's blade and reaches the point.

Spine

This is the unsharpened top part of the knife. Essentially, it is the blunt side that allows people to use their fingers to press down on the knife.

Edge

The entire sharp part of the blade. Some knives have a single edge while others have a double edge.

Serrations

Some blades have a sawtooth-like design on the edge of the knife. These designs are often called serrations.

Blade

The blade is the sharp region of the knife that includes the edge, point, serrations, spine, and belly.

Bevel

When you look at a knife, then you will notice a slight incline that leads to the edge of the knife. This incline is called the bevel. The higher your bevels are, the more cutting power your knife has.

Tang

The back portion of the knife. Essentially, this is the 'handle' part of the knife without the actual handle attached to it.

Handle

The handle is the covering for the tang. The handle can be made out of wood or leather.

Pin

Not all knives have pins, but they can be spotted easily on the handle of the blade. They are the small spots on the blade which you add to secure the handle to the tang.

Advanced Anatomy

Ricasso

This is the thick part of the knife that lies between the blade and the handle. The ricasso is mainly used to provide extra reinforcement of the knife.

Pommel

This is the butt of the knife, and sometimes, you might find knifemakers turn it into a unique design or a cap-like formation.

Quillons

These are protrusions from the handle. You will find a pair of these, one on the pommel and one between the ricasso and the handle. They are usually created to prevent the hand from sliding up and down the handle. Can also be referred to as the guard if you see them only formed between the ricasso and the handle.

Quillons are usually designed on only one side of the knife. A guard is formed on both sides of the handle such that if you hold the knife vertically, it will look like a cross. In fact, a better way to imagine this part is to imagine a vertical knife. The horizontal section that goes across the knife is the guard.

Bolster

With some knives, you might notice a thick junction between the handle of the knife and the blade. This thick section is used to provide a smooth transition from the tang to the blade and is called bolster.

Choil

Some knives have a slight depression between the edge and the ricasso. Such a depression is known as a choil.

Knowing the Knife

When you know the different parts of the knife, then it becomes easy for you to design your knife. Do you need a pommel? Are you planning to make a double-edged knife or a single-edge? Since you are a beginner, can you make the guard easily or would you like to try making a knife without a guard first?

By recognizing different parts of the knife, you will be able to create one that fits your idea. Additionally, when you want to make changes to a specific section of a knife, then you will know the name of the part you are focusing on. This becomes important when you are trying to describe your knife to someone else.

Blade Profiles

Different knives will be better suited for various tasks, depending on their blade profile. The profile is the term used to describe the overall shape of the blade and gives the blade its look. Learning the basic blade profiles can serve as a guide while designing your blade based on the specific functions you want it to serve.

One of the most common blade profiles is the drop point, which is favored as the best style for survival and hunting blades. A drop point is characterized by the spine of the blade "dropping" down from the handle to the tip, with the tip at the center axis of the blade. The spine extends the full length of the tip, which makes it much stronger and less prone to breaking. It also makes an excellent knife for carving.

A clip point blade is another common type of blade profile and is named after the "clipped off" appearance of the tip of the blade. The tip is sharper and thinner and, therefore, more suited for stabbing and piercing. However, this thin tip also makes it much weaker than a drop point blade, and it tends to break more easily.

A tanto profile is sometimes used in a military-style design and fighting utility knives. This profile has a spine that slopes slightly down to a point that is sharp and angular. This makes for a blade with a tip that is great for piercing, stabbing, and general utility.

A spearpoint design has a point that meets in the middle of two symmetrical sides, much like the tip of a spear. A spearpoint can have either one or both edges sharpened and has a strong and sharp point. This feature makes it a great knife for piercing or stabbing. However, it's very difficult to do any fine carving or detail work with, and it isn't a practical daily-use knife.

Designing a Knife

There are a few things that you should remember when you are designing your knife.

When you are designing a knife, make sure you know what you will primarily use it for. This helps you understand how you would like to design the edge, whether you need a guard, what kind of point you should create, and other useful information. A lot of people who start making knives think that they would like to design a knife that can achieve practically every purpose. But such a knife does not exist. Designing a knife in a particular manner means that you have to make sacrifices in other areas.

To make a knife, you will require a knife template. The best way to learn how to make a template is to see it in the process. So, here are the steps to create your very own knife template. In this template, we are going to create a simple hunting knife.

On a piece of printer paper, draw two horizontal lines that are no more than 2 inches apart. Since you are getting started, use a width of 1¼ inch. Between these two lines, you have to create your knife.

The overall length of the knife should not be more than 15 inches. However, with our measurements, the knives won't even be that long.

Let's focus on the blade first. A 4-inch blade might be too long for some and anything that falls below 3¼ inches might be too short. Mainly, you should keep the blade length at 3⅞ inches or if that seems too precise, then make the blade between 3¼ and 4 inches long.

Creating the handle is tricky since different people have different hand sizes. But what you should do is form a handle that balances the blade. At this point, you should ideally be looking to create a handle that is about 4 inches long. Some knife makers can go up to 4¼ inches long for the handle, but you should remain within the 4 ¼ inch mark.

Creating a Template

Draw out your knife. This drawing will eventually be your knife, so take your time and play around with the design.

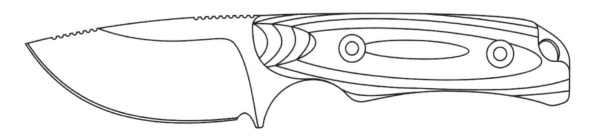

Figure 4: A simple knife template

If you want to get the printable version of this knife template for FREE, go to **bit.ly/sellknives**, and enter your e-mail.

When you settle on a final design, make a photocopy to keep as a reference. Then, cut out the paper knife and glue it onto a piece of wood using spray adhesive.

Using a band saw, or hacksaw, carefully cut out the design onto the piece of wood. Fine-tune the template by using a wood file to get rid of the saw marks and shape your knife by taking away everything up to the edge of the drawing. The more precise you are, the more you'll get a feel for what your knife will be like.

Hold the template in your hand and get a feel for it. Does the handle need to be longer or shorter? Is the blade length what you're looking for? Are the blade length and handle length the right proportions? If you have any doubts in the design, this is the time to fix it. It takes far less time to make a new template than to try to fix design flaws in your blade as you're working.

CHAPTER 3: MAKING A KNIFE BY STOCK REMOVAL

In this chapter, we are going to learn how to make a knife using a method that is ideal for beginners; stock removal.

We have already created the template for the hunting knife in the previous chapter. The topic of grinding bevels and heat treatment are explained in more detail, later in this book.

As we had mentioned before, we are going to start off by using the 1084 blade. We already know the dimensions of our knife, so it should be relatively easy to discover the dimensions of the steel as well.

For your knife, use a 1084 steel that is 9 inches long. This way, even if you decide to make the blade 4 inches and the handle 4¼ inches, you will have plenty of space to work with. The width of the metal that you choose should be no more than 2 inches.

If you find yourself in possession of steel that is longer and wider than the dimensions you have chosen, then all you have to do is use your trusty angle grinder to cut off the extra parts. To cut them off, draw the dimensions of the steel (9 inches x 2 inches) and cut along the lines. Try not to waste any of the extra metal as you could use it for making more knives. The best way to work with all the extra metal is by drawing grids of your steel dimensions. For example, if you have 1084 steel that is 10 inches long and about 6 inches wide, then technically, you can make 3 x (9 inches x 2 inches sized) blades. You will have one very narrow strip remaining in the end, which you can keep aside for future projects. You can still make knives out of the remaining metal. However, they might be narrower than the ones you are making right now.

You can even draw out the shape of your knife on the blade itself to help you understand how to get the shape that you want.

Once you have done that, follow the steps below:

1. Typically, you might find out that your steel comes with the run-of-the-mill (no pun intended) mill scale. When you use metals, they should ideally have a smoke gray color. But with a mill scale coating, you can end up having a dark gray layer. There are two ways of removing the mill scale, the mechanical method, and the chemical method.
2. In the mechanical method, you use your belt grinder to slowly chip away at the layer until you can finally see the mill scale removed. You can use a 50 or 60 grit belt for a rough grit and then move up to 100 grit belt for a final grit.
3. The chemical method is the easier method, but it takes a while to get all the coating off. First, you will need the below items:
   a. A 2-gallon bucket
   b. 2 x 5-gallon bucket
   c. Chemical resistance gloves
   d. Safety goggles
   e. White vinegar (you need enough to make sure that your steel is completely submerged into the vinegar)
4. When you are ready, take one 5-gallon bucket and then pour the white vinegar into it.

a. Next, take the 2-gallon bucket and drill some holes at the bottom using your handheld drill.

b. Take the piece of metal that you would like to descale and then place it inside the 5-gallon bucket that has the white vinegar in it.

c. You now have to wait for at least 24 hours. During that time, keep turning the metal around every 4 hours so that the vinegar can reach every part of the metal.

d. Do not dip your hands directly into the vinegar. It might not be as dangerous as other forms of acid, but it still has a burn to it. Also, make sure that you are using goggles to protect your eyes from splashes when moving around the metal.

e. As you can see, this method of descaling is rather long, but it involves less activity, and you can use it when you have a busy day ahead of you.

f. When you finally take out the steel from the bucket, you only need to hose it down with water to remove any traces of mill scale. If you find any stubborn mill scales, you can use the belt grinder, but you won't be putting a lot of effort into it. The mill scales usually come off within a minute or less of subjecting it to the grinder.

g. You can also fill the second 5-gallon bucket with water and use that to take off any traces of the white vinegar. Lift the 2-gallon bucket, wait for the white vinegar to drain, and transfer it to the 5-gallon bucket with water for a quick wash before you hose or grind of the mill scale.

h. The alternative to using vinegar is muriatic acid. However, I would not recommend using muriatic acid for beginners because the acid is highly toxic. In fact, they are so toxic that you will have to use respirators or your lungs will burn by inhaling even a small portion of the acid fumes. Plus, they are tough to handle and might need a lot of extra precautions. So in the interest of safety, let's try and avoid industrial grade acid as much as possible.

i. If you would like to buy metal with no mill scale deposits on it, then you should ideally be looking to get cold-rolled steel. But you will be spending quite a bit to get your hands on cold-rolled steel.

5. Once you have removed the mill scale, use a clamp to keep the steel in place. Then use your hacksaw to cut out a rough shape of the knife. You can also use an angle grinder for the job. Regardless of what tool you use, make sure that you are well protected, and you are careful when using the tools. Prudence is your best course of action, especially since you are a beginner.

6. Your next step is to clean up the knife using your belt sander. This means that you are going to get the shape more refined and accurate. For this purpose, we are going to use a 60 grit belt, since all we want to do at this point is to refine the shape we have already created.

7. You are now ready to add a bevel to the knife. At this point, it will be a little rough. Go ahead and mark the bevel and edge on your knife using any marker. Then you run the knife on the belt sander/grinder until you get the edge that you want. Essentially, you need to mark the center of your knife or the point from where you edge begins. Make sure that when you are adding your bevel, you keep the part towards the center or the point of origin of the bevel thick.

8. There are 3 different types of bevels you can choose from: flat grind, convex grind, or hollow grind. The full guide to doing this is given later in the book.

9. Now that you have given the knife its shape, it is now time to drill holes in the tang. You should always do this before going into the heat treatment process. You can use any drill for creating the holes, but the drill press gives you greater control and accuracy because you can hold the knife in place while you make the holes.

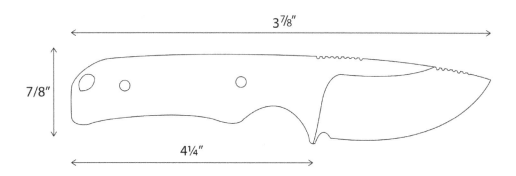

Figure 5: The knife template with measurements

10. Time to heat-treat the metal. The instructions are for 1084 steel. Place it into the forge and allow the steel to heat until it enters the yellow range (or in other words, when the metal turns bright yellow). You are aiming to get the metal to a non-magnetic point. If you would like to check if you have successfully done this, place a magnet nearby and see if the metal attracts it. When you have reached the non-magnetic temperature, then keep the metal in the forge for about 15 minutes. Full heat treatment instructions are given in the following chapters.

11. You are now going to quench the metal. Make sure that you have canola oil that has been heated to 135°F, to use as the quenchant. At the end of those 15 minutes where you placed the metal into the forge, transfer it directly to the canola oil. As we had mentioned before, make sure you have a lid ready nearby in case you need it.

12. Once you have finished quenching the metal, take it out for the tempering process. Preheat your oven to around 400°F. Place the metal into the oven for about two hours. Take out the metal, allow it to cool. Then place it back into the oven for another two hours. You can also make use of a blowtorch if you have one. Or you can use a toaster (make sure the entire blade fits into the toaster).

13. After completing the tempering process, it is time to remove the scales from heat heat treatment and finalize the bevels. Head back to your grinder and then add the finishing touches. Grind down the knife to the thickness that you want. You will notice that at this point, your knife looks more and more like the knife that you had in mind.

14. Your knife is now ready for the gluing process. To glue the handles on the knife, use epoxy to get the job done. One of the popular epoxies that you can find in the market is T-88, but you are welcome to use any brand that you are comfortable using.

15. Shape your handle using the belt sander.

16. Polish your blade using sandpaper.

17. Finish it off by sharpening it.

A Couple of Tips to Remember

- You can also drill holes into the knife design that you made on the steel bar before using a hacksaw to cut it. This is because it is much easier to clamp down a rectangular piece of steel, as compared to a knife blank.
- When you are working on the belt sander, make sure that your tool rest is as close to the belt as possible. If it is not, then there is a possibility that the belt with catch the knife, wrestle it in between, and harm your fingers in the process.

CHAPTER 4: FORGING A KNIFE (FULL TANG KNIFE)

Before we go into the actual process of forging, it is better to understand a bit about the process.

After all, you have your workspace all set up, your design laid out, and a piece of steel ready to go. At this point, you should make sure all your tools are where you can have easy access to them, place your blade in the forge, and get it cranking.

To properly work your blade, you'll need to take it out of the forge when it's at an appropriate temperature. While it's possible to buy a thermometer for a propane forge, most people gauge the right temperature and the degree of workability of the metal by its color.

Here is a table to help you understand the color and the temperature of the metal when it attains that color. Use this as a reference whenever you work with your metal.

Fahrenheit	The Color of the Steel	Process
2,000°	Bright Yellow	Forging
1,900°	Dark Yellow	Forging
1,800°	Orange Yellow	Forging
1,700°	Orange	Forging
1,600°	Orange Red	Forging
1,500°	Bright Red	Forging
1,400°	Red	Forging
1,300°	Medium Red	-
1,200°	Dull Red	-
1,100°	Slight Red	-
1,000°	Mostly Grey	-
800°	Dark Grey	Tempering

575°	Blue	Tempering
540°	Dark Purple	Tempering
520°	Purple	Tempering
480°	Brown	Tempering
445°	Light Straw	Tempering

Remember that when you are using the table, you don't have to get the exact shade of the color mentioned above. Typically, if you get an orange-yellow or orange shade, then you have reached the orange temperature range. Which is why you might always hear bladesmiths mention that they heat the metal to a particular range.

We are going to use the same knife design that we created in Chapter 2. If you haven't designed the knife already, go ahead and create the design now.

Once again, we are going to use a steel that is 9 inches long and 2 inches wide. This time, however, we are going to use 1095 high carbon steel.

We are going to begin by de-scaling the steel. The method to de-scale is taught in Chapter 3. After you have completed de-scaling the steel, here are the steps that you need to take to forge it.

Here are a couple of things to remember:

- Steel needs to undergo changes during heating to become malleable (or flexible in layman terms, but we do not use the term flexible here as it might indicate the metal can be stretched). If you try to hit a piece of steel that's too cold, you'll only be working the outer layers of the metal, and you'll get a unique effect that looks like mushroom shapes taking place on the metal.
- It's also possible to get too high of a temperature, which is most likely when using a coal forge. As a beginner, you should start with the propane forge but if you are already using the coal forge, then make sure that you are careful and not overheating the metal. Here is a tip for you to follow when you are using a coal-based forge: take care to arrange your coals so that you can lay your steel across the fire evenly. If you concentrate the heat towards the knife to a particular area, then it is possible to melt the tip of your knife entirely off. Or an easier method is to, of course, use a propane forge!

A Game Plan

Before you start hammering, you need to come up with a game plan. Your steel will begin to cool down immediately when you take it out of the forge, and every time you place it on the anvil, it rapidly draws heat away through conduction. This means you only have about six to eight good hammer strikes before you need to put it back in again to heat up. So if you are in the process of shaping the metal, then you have to be precise with your strikes. Use your time wisely! Take a good look at your steel and plan exactly where you'll be hitting it before you put it back in the forge. Make a mental plan of the steps you'll be taking so that you don't have to waste any time trying to figure that out when your blade is heated and ready to work. If you do have to stop hammering for a moment, hold the steel up instead of letting it rest on the anvil to prevent unnecessary cooling.

As a beginner, your ability to make accurate strikes on the metal is unlikely. You might not be able to get the shape that you want quickly. But that is okay. Take as much time as you need and place the metal into the forge through multiple cycles to form the shape you had in your mind.

There are no mistakes here, merely lessons to be learned while you work the forge.

Working With Steel

It's useful to think of the hot steel as clay. Imagine hitting clay with your hammer and what would happen to it as you delivered blows. While steel will be a lot harder to move than clay, the basic principles are the same. As you apply force, the malleable steel will move away from that force in the direction of least resistance. As you work, you will be adjusting where you are striking with your hammer as well as the direction of your strike. In this manner, you can control not only the force but where the steel will have a tendency to move by manipulating the path of least resistance.

As you work, the steel will eventually bend up at the ends, losing its flatness. It seems like common sense to want to hammer on the upturned ends to flatten the steel again, but this doesn't allow you to apply the right kind of force. By flipping the steel over and striking it in the middle, both ends will be pushed flat against the anvil as the middle moves away from the force of your hammer. Keep an eye on the steel as you work. Use the last strike or two to ensure your steel stays as flat as possible.

Now we are going to see how you can use the forge to give shape to the knife.

1. The first thing you are going to do is figure out where the knife's tip is going to be. Since we are not going to be using the hacksaw and grinding the knife, we are going to be using the forge to shape out the knife.
2. Heat the steel until it reaches the yellow temperature range.
3. Once it reaches the temperature, use your tongs to take out the steel. Now you are going to hold the steel on the anvil. Hold it in a way that the future cutting edge of the knife is facing down.
4. Hit the top corner at a 45° angle. This is because we are going to start with the knife's drop point, which is an easy way to create the knife point. As you strike, you'll notice the steel mushrooming out. When you see this happen, then place the steel on its sides and hammer it until the mushroom shape disappears.

Figure 6: Forging the right knife is all about patience and careful understanding of the technique.

1. Go back to the previous position and continue hammering the steel at a 45° angle.
2. Keep repeating this process until you have what looks like the profile of the knife tip pounded in.
3. Currently, the point or tip of the knife will be positioned more towards where the edge of the knife should be. This tip will change position as you continue to move the metal, moving from the bottom of the blade to the top. The natural tendency of the metal is to push things away as it gets thinner, which is why, as you begin working on the edge, this tip or point will end up rising to the top of the blade, closer to the blade's spine level.

So if you start getting worried about why your point is not in the correct position, don't! We still have a lot of steps to go.

4. So back to the knife. We are now going to work on the knife's edge.
5. Look at your steel again and decide how long you want the cutting edge of your knife to be. This is based on the total length of the knife's blade. So you should have placed it anywhere between 3¼ inches and 4 inches long.
6. Once you have decided the length of the knife, heat it again until it reaches the yellow temperature range.
7. Here is a trick that you can use to make a mark on the blade so that you will know where the blade of the knife begins. Hold the blade over the edge of the anvil and hit one side of it (the spindle side of the knife) of it with the hammer to make a small indented mark on the cutting edge side of the blade. This mark will let you know where the handle of the blade starts from (make sure that you are using your measurements to decide where this mark should be). You can choose to remove this mark later during the forging process (it happens as you work on the metal) or alternatively, many bladesmiths make the indentation deeper and make a choil out of it. For now, we are going to focus on how to make a basic knife without the choil.
8. Now that you know the edge. It is time to hammer it out and make it look sharp!
9. **Tip:** Use a little bit of water on the anvil. This will help blow out the knife scale, with each hammer blow.

10. Holding your steel flat on the anvil, pound along the edge. Flip the metal and hammer on the same part from the other side. This will cause the metal here to thin out and will begin to create the bevels of your knife. Notice how, as you thin the edge, the tip will slowly start moving up towards the spine side of the knife. This means that you are going to get the point to the proper place.

11. As you make progress with your blade, keep an eye on its overall shape. In addition to maintaining overall flatness, you'll have to work to keep the spine of your blade straight as well. As you notice it losing its straightness, flip the blade onto its edge so that the spine is on the anvil. Now hammer the spine until you see it becoming straight. But won't this affect the edge as well? Of course, it will! In which case, flip the knife onto its side and hammer the edge back to its correct shape. You need to constantly correct the shapes of either parts of the blade.

12. As you keep working on the metal, you will notice that it will get a rough shape. You don't have to work until the edge is truly sharp. All you are doing is getting a rough outline of the final knife that you are going to work on.

13. Once you get a rough shape, shift your attention to the handle area, or tang. Hold the blade on its edge, with the spine side on the anvil.

14. Start hammering the knife from the part where your indentation starts (the one you used to mark the start of the blade). Once again, hammer the side of the blade to remove the mushrooming effect that the metal gains during the process. Before working on the tang, the edge and the tang will look like they are connected. Once you start hammering the knife, the tang will form a handle shape, the metal getting narrower.

15. By now, you should be able to see the full shape of your knife starting to form. Use the techniques you've learned to try to focus on areas that show mistakes and further refine the profile of your knife. There's no substitution for time and learning from your mistakes, so don't be afraid if you make them. Every mistake is an opportunity to learn.

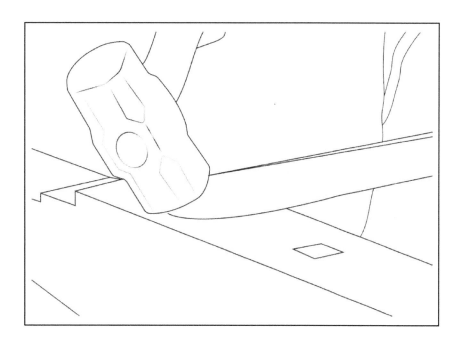

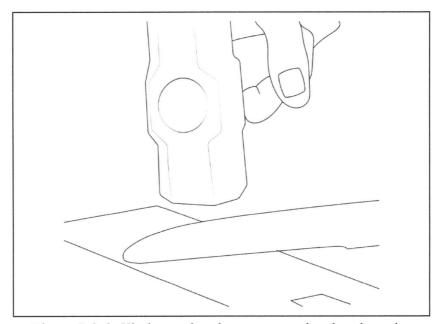

Figure 7 & 8: Hit the steel at the corners to develop the point

1. Once you have completed the profile of your knife and you are satisfied with the results, let's move on to making holes in the tang.

2. You have already seen how you can make holes using the drill. But since your knife is hot, how can you create these holes right now? What you do is use a technique called the hot punch. How does it work? Let's find out.

3. The first thing that you are going to want to do is get yourself a hot punch, which is like a pointed and elongated piece of steel. Look at the pointed end of the hot punch and check out how narrow or broad it is. This will let you know how big the hole on the tang will be.

4. When you are ready, heat the knife's tang until it reaches the yellow range in temperature. Once the temperature is right, place the knife on the anvil. Focus on where you would like to create a hole in the tang. Place the hot punch on top of that position and strike it a few times. Flip the knife over with the tongs, and you will be able to notice a small dark spot where the punch struck the knife on the other side. Place the punch over this dark spot and hit it with the hammer. Continue this process until you literally 'punch' out the piece of metal from the tang and create a hole. Make sure to take the hot punch out quickly after hammering, so that it does not get stuck in the hole and join with the knife.

5. Repeat this step with the rest of the holes that you would like to create on the knife.

6. At this point, you might notice that your knife might have some scaling on it. Head over to the grinder and remove the scales (you can also use the white vinegar method, but at this point, the scales won't be too challenging to remove).

7. Once we have accomplished all of that, it is time to move on to the next step: grinding bevels!

CHAPTER 5: GRINDING GOOD BEVEL LINES

Now that making the knife blank is done, it's time to start grinding. After the profile of your knife is refined, you'll be removing layers of knife material to create bevels. These will form an angle that makes the cutting edge of your blade.

You could say that this is the defining moment in which you turn your piece of steel into a knife. Does that sound exciting? Well, let's get started. But before that, we should understand a little more about grinding.

There's a variety of tools and techniques you can use to create these grinds, and your choice will depend on your own experience and preference. Professional knifemakers make this step look easy, but it takes a lot of practice to develop their level of comfort and skill. The trick is to go slow, be patient with yourself, and put in plenty of time behind the grinder.

Before you start making the angles, make sure your blade profile is all set. You can remove any large pieces of steel outside your design with a hacksaw, band saw, or the cutting wheel of an angle grinder. If you worked your blade at the forge, then revisit the template and redraw your bevel line. Use a belt grinder, files, or angle grinder to remove all material that won't be part of your knife's final shape.

A quality grind on a knife is produced not only with great technique but with a basic understanding of blade geometry. A good blade has an appropriate balance between overall strength, sharpness, and edge retention suited for its intended use. Unfortunately, there's no one-size-fits-all knife grind. Understanding what factors affect the performance of your blade will help you to choose the best grind for your blade and allow you to have a specific goal in mind.

The first thing that you will notice is that there are different types of grinds that you can use for your blade. Here are the most popular ones:

Full Flat Grind

This grind is done in a V-shaped and works consistently from the spine to the edge. It creates a good balance of cutting ability and strength. While it is a very sharp grind, it can dull quickly but is easy to sharpen. This design is standard in kitchen knives.

Scandinavian Grind

Often used when making bushcraft knives, the Scandinavian grind - or Scandi grind for short - is a flat grind that starts below the halfway point of the blade. By leaving a lot of material in the spine of the blade, this grind can maximize the durability of your knife. The lack of a secondary bevel means that the low angle will create a sharp edge. While the edge is not as tough as other grinds that offer a secondary bevel, it does make it very easy to sharpen in the field, even for a beginner. It is an excellent grind for carving.

The location of the bevel makes it easy to see what you're doing, and a blade with a Scandi grind will be able to cut through most pieces of wood with relative ease.

Scandi

Sabre Grind

The sabre grind is a flat grind that starts halfway up the blade. While it isn't quite as good at carving, it tends to slice slightly better. Unlike the Scandi, the sabre grind typically has a secondary bevel.

Sabre
Grind

Hollow Grind

In this grind, the bevels curve in to form a thin, very sharp edge. This edge tends not to be as durable as some other grinds, and it tends to need a lot of retouching to stay sharp. This edge can be slightly more challenging to grind as a knifemaker, but the edge created isn't difficult to re-sharpen.

The incredible sharp edge of a hollow grind makes it the grind of choice for straight razors and hunting knives. It tends to bind up at the top of the hollow when slicing through materials such as cardboard and isn't as well suited to being a utility knife as some other grind styles.

Full
Hollow
Grind

Convex Grind

A convex grind is a rounded grind that focuses on the edge. The mass behind the edge increases the durability of the edge, and it can be quite sharp. This grind is often used in axes, machetes, or choppers.

Convex
Grind

Chisel Grind

In a chisel grind, one side of the cutting edge has a flat grind, while the other has no bevel ground in. Because of the shallow blade angle, a chisel grind makes an incredibly sharp edge. This sharp angle also means the edge doesn't have the best durability and needs to be continuously maintained. Chisel grinds are commonly used in food preparation as well as woodworking, as the bevel makes it easy to follow the wood grain. It can be slightly inaccurate when slicing, due to the edge being off-center. Knives made with this grind are often either right-handed blades or left-handed blades, depending on which side the bevel is on.

Chisel
Grind

Figures 9 to 13: Different grinds and their profiles

A Note Before Grinding

When you spend more time grinding, you develop an instinctual understanding of how your body needs to move to get the results you want. There is definitely a learning curve, so be patient with yourself. With a little bit more time, you won't need to think about your movements as much as when you're first starting.

Developing your grinding style is about consistency, so eliminate discomforts. Stand with a slightly wide-set but comfortable stance to give yourself a stable base. Keep your elbows tucked against your sides and lock them into your hips. Instead of using your arms to move the blade, move from your core. Shift your weight steadily in your hips and think about using controlled and calculated movements. By working to create a pattern in your movement, you will find a comfortable rhythm that will make grinding much more predictable.

Finally, make sure that you do not take any substantial risks. Be patient with your work and make sure that you are comfortable understanding the basics of grinding.

Creating a Grind

Let us work with the Scandi grind technique and then you can use the same ideas for the other grinds:

- The first thing that you need to do is create the bevel outline in the metal. To do this, take out a permanent marker and then find the center line of your cutting edge.
- Mark that outline. If you like, you can even color the entire edge of the blade using the marker.

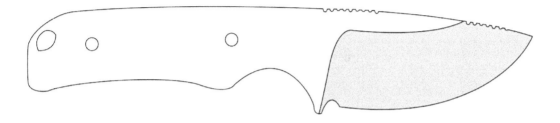

Figure 14: Mark the entire area you want to grind

- The next part is a little tricky, so make sure you read this instruction carefully before putting it to practice. Take a hand drill (or scribe) close to the outline of your blade (near the center) and run it along the flat surface, dragging the tip along the blade edge.
  - Let's imagine that you are creating a knife that is 2 inches wide. You have decided to draw the outline at the 1-inch mark.
  - You are going to use the drill to create a line just below the outline (this process is called scribing), allowing you to see where you would like the bevels to meet. Flip the blade and do the same thing again.
  - Now you can mark the bevel outline on the blade.
  - Alternatively, you can use only the outline for the purpose, but by creating a mark, you have a better idea of where you should start the bevel.
  - This step makes sure that the grinds will be symmetrical, and more resistant to warping after heat treatment.
- We are now going to take the knife to the grinder. If your grinder does not have a fresh belt, then it might be time to get one. This is because old belts heat up faster. However, you can still work using an old belt as well as it will teach you the effects of overheating, and when you should take the blade away from the belt. As for the belt grit, you can use a 50 grit belt for this purpose.
- Bring the steel toward the belt. Gently let the steel find the spot you've created for the edge and start moving the steel gently sideways. You don't need to place a ton of pressure on the blade; move it across and let the belt do its job.

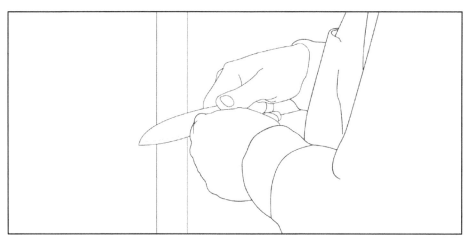

Figure 15: Sideways grinding

- Every time you take your steel off the grinder, assess how much material you need to take off and repeat the process. You should always have a clear idea of this before you grind again. Many knifemakers make the mistake of jumping back to grinding without a second thought, and end up either taking out too much material, or messing up the grind lines.
- Do not focus on one side only. Keep flipping the knife over to keep the grind lines even.
- Allow the grind to pass across the full length of the cutting edge, from the tip to just before the where the outline ends and the tang begins.
- Switch sides every few passes to keep the grind lines even.
  - o Some knifemakers start at the end of the outline and work their way toward the tip of the knife. Other makers do the complete opposite; starting from the tip and moving along the knife towards the tang. There is no right or wrong way here.
  - o Try working the blade both ways and see which you prefer. Remember, you are allowed to make as many mistakes as possible. Once you find the method that is comfortable for you, it will become easier for you in future grinds. But the only way you are going to find out the comfort point is by actually experimenting with different grinds!
- Another important tip to remember at this point: keep even pressure on the blade, and keep the steel moving. Check your progress every few passes. But do not be tempted to stop and check every few seconds, as this might cause the grinding process to give you a choppy line.
- Continue working your grind higher and higher up toward the spine. Every pass should be slightly higher than the last. Your grind lines should be as straight as possible.
- If you notice your line becoming wavy, try and check the amount of pressure you're putting on the blade and try to keep it consistent.
- If you find a specific area has less material taken off, try slowing down on those high spots and putting more pressure on the other side of the blade.
- Work on the blade slowly so that you can keep things even on both sides of the knife.
- Here is a tip you can use if you don't mind spending a little for different grits for your grinder.
  - o Start with a 50 grit belt and complete the grinding process until the previous step.

- o Once done, switch out your 50 grit belt for a 120 grit and color in the ground surface with a permanent marker again. Take your blade back to the grinder and start to clean up your grinds with the finer grit.
- o Keep working until the marker is completely removed and then repeat the process with a 220 grit.
- o This process of cleaning up the grind isn't only about the aesthetic of the blade but is a precautionary measure taken to prevent the blade from cracking or warping in the heat treat.
- o Any deep grooves, scratches, or sharp edges will be susceptible to cracking in the quench due to the stress created by this process. As a bonus, this will likely make the blade easier to clean up after the heat treatment process.

The Hollow Ground Edge

The hollow ground edge has a concave edge. This form of an edge is well suited to blades that will be mainly used for slicing. Examples of such blades include skinners, hunters, filet knives, etc.

The main reason why the hollow ground edge is suitable for such knives is the fact that it produces a very thin edge that can be sharpened quite easily. However, because of this thin edge, the blade can be somewhat fragile compared to other forms of grinds. This is why it is not prudent to make a hollow ground edge if you are going to be using your blade against heavier substances such as bone, wood, or materials with similar thickness. An important fact to know here is most of the blades produced around the world today are hollow ground. It could be because not many people are looking to cut bone or thicker materials!

Here is how you can achieve a hollow grind. Follow the steps in the process for the Scandi edge until you come to the part where you begin grinding. The process will be a little different for the Scandi grind.

- Take the blade and slowly bring the edge to the surface of the wheel of the belt.
- Now start the wheel of the belt and allow for the grind to form. Flip the knife over and then work on the other side. That is essentially the basics of the hollow grind edge. For beginners, getting the perfect grind might not be easy. However, with practice, you should be able to get the edge that you require.

The Flat Grind

The flat grind creates a nice balance between the hollow grind and the convex grind. One of the main advantages it provides is that, since it draws from both the hollow grind and the convex grind, it has an excellent edge that can bear the brunt of heavy chopping. Additionally, even after multiple chopping sessions, it can still retain its sharpness.

- The flat grind is similar to the hollow grind but is simpler to perform. This is because you are not focusing on the edge alone but on the entire blade.
- Your technique involves a process similar to the hollow grind. Bring the edge close to the grinding wheel or belt.
- When the edge is sharp, continue working on the blade towards the spine.
- Once you are done, you should notice a linear slope that starts from the edge and goes all the way to the spine.

The Convex Grind

A convex edge is where the blade has a bevel on each side that is slightly curved. Convex edges are said to be rather difficult to accomplish by hand. The ideal way to work on these grinds is by using a belt grinder. Here is how you can create this grind on your knife.

- For convex edges, we are first going to make sure that we leave off a little bit of thickness on the edge because we do not want it to get too thin.
- You want to start off by first flat-grinding the edge.
- Once you have completed the flat grind, you should then use a 60 grit belt on the grinder. You need to hold the knife at a slight angle, but not too much because you need the sides of the blade to touch the belt.

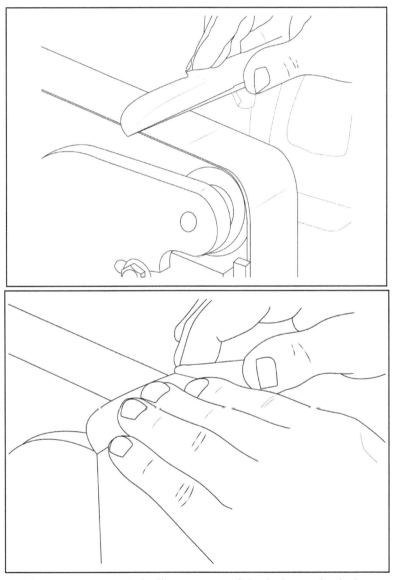

Figure 16 & 17: Grinding on top of the belt sander helps

- With that angle, bring the side of the blade to the belt and then start grinding.
- While grinding, you need to move the knife back and forth a little bit along the edge. Start doing this on one side and then flip the knife over. Continue grinding the knife on the other side at an angle.
- Flip the knife over every two rotations of the grind.
- Once you have completed the grind, you now have a convex shape along the side of the knife.
- Now we focus on the edge. Touch the edge lightly to the belt. Don't press down too much on it.
- Move the knife and allow the belt to form a nice convex edge.
- Flip the knife over and work on the edge from the other side.
- Eventually, you are going to achieve a nice convex edge.

Tips for Grinding

- Always remember to use your hips instead of your wrist while shifting grind lines. Aim to keep your elbows close to your sides, your shoulders back and your stomach tight. All of these simple adjustments will allow you to have better control over your grinding process.
- Be confident near the grinder. Keep your movements controlled and stable. As we had already seen, do not try to press against the grinder too hard.

How Thin Should The Edge Be?

Here is a common question that many knifemakers come across: how thin or thick should the knife-edge be? What you should look for is the purpose of the knife.

The general rule of thumb is that thicker blades are used to cut harder materials. You might use them for cutting wood or skinning game. On the other hand, a thinner knife is used for slicing, like the kitchen knives.

So how thick or thin should your knife edge be? Well, if you are using it for hunting purposes, then you should make it about 1.5mm thick. If you intend to slice through things and need the right sharpness for it, then your knife edge should be about 0.3mm.

CHAPTER 6: HEAT TREATING

Essentially, no material or finished product can be manufactured without sending it through the process of heat treating. In this process, a particular metal is heated to a high temperature and then cooled under specific conditions to improve its characteristics, stability, and performance.

Through heat treatment, you can soften a metal, which allows the metal to become more flexible. You can also use heat treatment to harden metals, ensuring that their strength is improved.

Heat treatment is essential if you are in the business of manufacturing parts for automobiles, aircrafts, computers, heavy machinery, and tools. In other words, if you want something important built, then you need to subject the material to heat treatment.

Iron, and more specifically, steel, are the most common materials that go through heat treatment. However, that does not mean that other materials cannot be treated with heat. By other materials, we mean your knife.

In short, this process is quite important, and you are going to learn to use it. But more importantly, let us look at each process and try to understand what it means.

Tempering

One of the processes of heat treatment is called tempering. In this process, you are basically altering the mechanical attributes (usually the flexibility and strength) of steel or products and items made from steel. Tempering releases the carbon molecules confined in the steel to diffuse from martensite. Martensite is a form of a crystalline structure consisting of brittle carbon that exists in hardened steel. Because of martensite's features, the steel may be hard, but it also becomes brittle, rendering it useless in most applications.

Tempering allows the internal stresses that may have been formed due to past uses to be discharged from the steel. This results in the alloy becoming more durable.

So how does one temper their steel? Firstly, the steel is heated to a high temperature, but it is not allowed to heat up beyond its melting point. Once that is done, it is then cooled in air. There is no fixed temperature for all forms of steel. They each have their own temperature range that must be reached first.

When you temper the steel, it is important to heat it gradually until it reaches the temperature you would like to work with. This prevents the metal from cracking.

Annealing

Annealing is another process of heat treatment, focused on softening the steel or reducing the hardness of the material. This is done so that it is easier to machine the steel.

In this process, the metal is heated to a temperate where it is possible to attain re-crystallization. This means that new non-deformed grains take over the positions of the deformed grains. And what exactly are grains? In metallurgy, each grain is a single crystal that consists of a specific arrangement of atoms. When you have deformed grains, then you cannot work on the metal without causing more deformity. In this case, the deformity appears in the form of cracks. When you perform the annealing process, you are forming new grains, which means you are allowing yourself to work on the metal again.

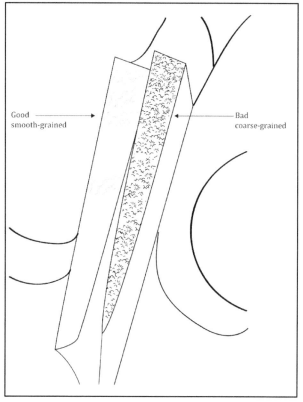

Figure 18: Good Grain vs Bad Grain

Normalizing

During normalizing, you are refining the size of the grain in the metal. After normalizing, the mechanical properties of the metal are improved.

Normalizing sets a uniformity to the structure of grains in the metal. After you have achieved uniformity, you have reduced the degree of deformity of the metal. This allows you to get a smooth finish and a wonderful product in the end.

Normalizing is usually used to remove the stresses built up inside a piece of steel and bring it back to its initial state.

In the process of normalizing, steel is heated to a high temperature and then cooled by leaving the metal at room temperature. This process of rapidly heating the metal and then slowly cooling it down makes changes in the microstructure of the alloy, making it elastic and durable. Normalizing is almost like a process of correction. This is because it is typically used when some other process unintentionally increases the hardness but decreases the malleability of the metal. What makes normalizing different from other methods such as annealing is that it uses room temperature to cool down the metal, rather than any medium or special technique.

Heat Treatment for 1084 steel

1084 has a somewhat higher manganese composition than other carbon steels in the 10XX category. Because it is a relatively easy steel to work with, it makes 1084 an ideal steel for beginners who want to start their bladesmithing adventure. It gives you enough room to make errors when it comes to heat treatment. It is known to form an almost complete 'pearlite' structure when you subject it to annealing and normalizing processes. Pearlite is a structure that features alternating layers.

Additionally, 1084 contains nearly 0.84% carbon (which is represented by the 84 in 1084) and is known to produce a good quality knife with a nice edge. Below is the full working sequence for 1084 steel.

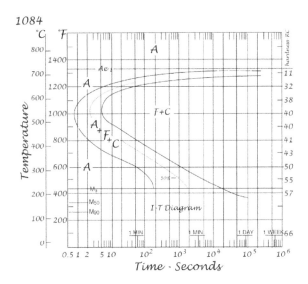

Figure 19: TTT graph of 1084 steel

Forging

You start by forging using the steps mentioned in Chapter 4. Once you have forged the knife, you can then move on to the heat treatment, beginning with the annealing process.

Normalizing

For the normalizing process, you heat the metal to 1600°F in a forge. Do not attempt to work on the metal below 1500°F. Once the temperature has been reached, soak the metal at the same temperature for about four minutes.

After four minutes, allow the metal to cool in still air. When you normalize the steel, you are resetting the crystalline structure. Through this reset, you are distributing the carbides in such a manner that they become uniform.

When you are working with steel, having an uneven structure affects its quality. Which is why, if you do not reset the structure, the carbides tend to group together tightly. Due to this, the steel will not have the sharp uniform edge that it could have had.

Annealing

In the annealing process, you start by heating the metal to 1500°F. Then you have to cool the metal, but you should avoid cooling it too quickly. You have to ensure that the metal cools at a rate of 50°F per hour or lower. I would not recommend going below 45°F for this purpose.

Pro Tip: In many cases, knife makers use an overnight cooling strategy. For this, you heat the metal to the required temperature of 1500°F at the end of the day. Ensure that the last heat of the day is slowly disappearing when you remove the metal from the forge. Once that is done, you then cool the metal in the forge overnight. This becomes handy when you have to perform other work, or you might be engaged in the evening.

At this point, you can perform your machining or grinding process, should you wish to.

Hardening

For this, you heat the steel to 1500°F. Or you can aim to push it past its non-magnetic limit. In this case, that limit is around 1425°F.

When you are working in the forge, you have to heat the metal until the metal does not attract a magnet to itself. When you have reached such a state, you heat it to a slightly higher temperature. This is just to make sure that you have truly pushed the steel into the non-magnetic area.

If you overheat the steel by keeping it at temperatures of 1550°F or beyond and you quench the metal, the metal could form grains.

To understand why grains cause harm, it is important to first understand more about grains themselves.

We all know chemistry 101; all metals are made up of atoms. Why is this important? Well, when you take a metal, then they are made up of tiny crystals of different orientations, based on the metal that you are using. These crystals are what you call grains. When you examine a single grain, then you will notice that the atoms are arranged in a particular orientation. This particular orientation can be found in every single grain of that metal.

Initially, grains do not cause any problems. However, grains tend to increase and when they do, they begin to affect the toughness of the blade. Bigger grains promote a brittle foundation, creating a knife that you might not be too proud of.

Therefore, the best way to complete this process is by heating it to its non-metallic temperature. Then keep it in the forge at that temperature for about a minute. Then remove the steel and quench it. Certain areas of the steel might only require about 1 or 2 seconds of cooling. However, that does not mean that you have to take the steel out of the forge and quickly dip in it liquid. Do not do that! Trust me that is a safety hazard. Think of it this way.

You take the metal out. You are in such a hurry to beat the 2-second mark that you knock off the oil to the ground. The metal drops, and there is a pretty big flare. That flare catches nearby furniture or object that is flammable. Well, you know the rest.

Do not be in a hurry. The steel will hold on to some of the heat and survive for a few seconds when introduced to the air. Take it carefully and place it into the liquid for quenching. Be ready to face a small flare-up along with a high level of smoke.

Quenching

1084 doesn't need a fast quenching oil. You can use canola oil for quenching 1084. Preheat the canola oil to about 135°F. Once done, quench the metal for about 10-15 seconds.

Tempering

If you have been following the instructions, then your steel should be around 65RC. At this level, it is fairly fragile, so do not drop it. It might shatter upon hitting the ground.

Tempering Temperature		Rockwell Hardness
°C	°F	HRC
149	300	65
177	350	63-64
204	400	60-61
232	450	57-58
260	500	55-56
288	550	53-54
316	600	52-53
343	650	50

Rockwell Hardness Scale for 1084 steel

We need to bring the hardness of the steel down to about 59 HRC. Bring the steel to room temperature and begin tempering it once it reaches that temperature. Heat the steel to a little bit above 400°F. Temper twice. Each tempering process should be done for two hours. Allow the steel to return to room temperature between the two processes. Ideally, your method should follow this sequence: temper for two hours, then return to room temperature, and then back to tempering.

Heat Treatment for 1095 steel

Working with 1095 steel is pretty simple. It is a steel with a high carbon content, and you can use it to forge shapes easily. It does have lower traces of manganese than other steel that are part of the 10XX series (such as the 1080 steel.) However, the comparatively higher rate of carbon means that it provides more carbide that can be used for providing resistance to abrasions. However, this also means that because of the extra carbon, you might have to put in more care during the heat treatment.

If you are going to heat treat 1095 steel, I would suggest that you have a temperature controlled forge.

But let's go through all the steps in the process so that you can understand what is happening. Given below is the total working sequence for 1095 steel.

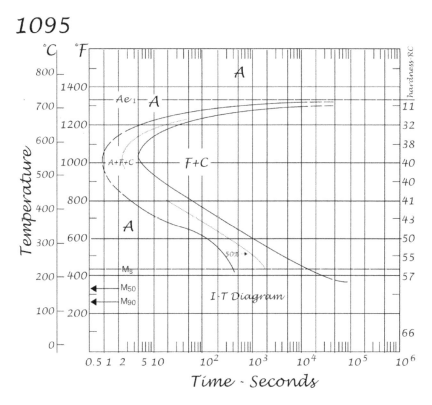

Figure 20: TTT graph of 1095 steel

Forging

We first start with the forging process. Take 1095 through the forging process that was mentioned earlier.

Normalizing

To normalize the steel, you have to bring the temperature of the metal to 1575°F. Let the metal sit inside the forge at that precise temperature, for 5 minutes. Once the 5 minutes are over, allow the metal to cool in the air till it reaches room temperature.

Another way to normalize is a little bit tricky. Get to 1575°F and choke your forge so it spits flames out of the opening and turn down the gas. It should maintain the same color inside as it did when you reached 1575°F.

Annealing

For the annealing process, you start by heating the metal to 1475°F. Cooling should be at a rate no faster than 50°F per hour.

The easiest way to cool the steel is by placing the blade inside a container of insulating, fireproof material. Wood ash is easily obtainable and a great insulator. Another option frequently used by knifemakers is vermiculite. Vermiculite is a mineral often used in gardening and can be found at any store that sells gardening supplies.

You could also go with the suggestion to cool it overnight. You have to keep the metal inside the forge to ensure the cooling is complete.

At this point, you can perform your machining or grinding process.

Grinding and Machining the Steel

You can use any of the grinding techniques that were mentioned in the previous chapter at this point.

Hardening

Heat to 1475°F which is the non-magnetic level of the knife. You can also heat just past that temperature, but ideally, stick to not going beyond that temperature. As explained before, this non-magnetic range of the temperature means that a magnet doesn't stick to the metal. Do not overheat the steel beyond 1550°F range. After heating move on to the quenching process.

Quenching

1095 steel requires a fast quenching oil. For this reason, the safest option that you can pick for 1095 steel is a special quenching oil. One of the more common oils in the market that I recommend is the Parks 50 quench oil. Parks 50 is a fast quench and is almost as fast as water. For this reason, make sure you don't grind your knife too thin before heat treatment. You start off by first preheating the oil to 70-120°F. Put the blade into the oil for about 7-9 seconds, until you notice that the hissing and bubbling subsides. Once done, take out the knife from the oil. You can also make use of quenching oil manufactured by Maxim Oil.

Finally, you can use canola oil, but that's only if you can't procure Parks 50. I only recommend using it on thin 1095 stock, up to about 1/8 inch. You could do it for ¼ inch stock, but I haven't done it personally, so I can't tell you how well it'd work.

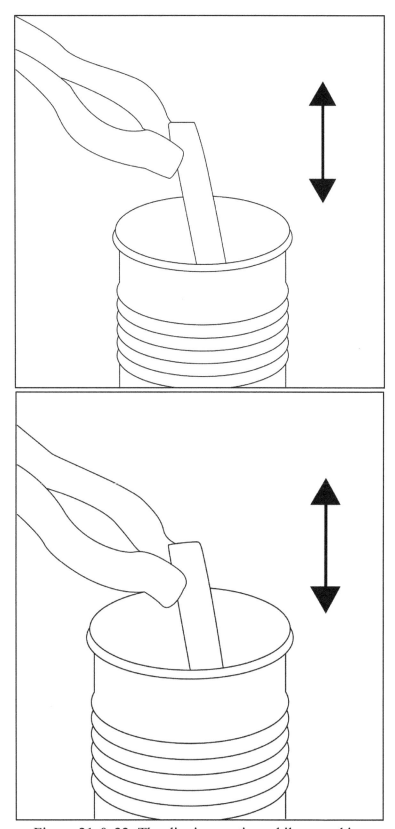

Figure 21 & 22: The dipping motion while quenching

When it comes to canola oil, preheat the oil to 135°F. Quench the knife in the liquid for about 10-15 seconds.

Tempering

The tempering process for 1095 steel is simple. Place the steel in an oven, and heat the steel to 500°F. We are trying to achieve about 59-60 HRC.

This will allow the knife to have good performance in most situations. However, I would still not recommend that you drop it. You might not destroy it entirely, but you might cause cracks to appear. Temper it twice for two hours each. Make sure that you are allowing it to cool. Bring it down to room temperature before you temper it again.

Cryo Treatment

Now, this step is not entirely necessary. However, it will improve the quality of the steel you are working with. If you like, you can skip this step altogether.

Soak the steel in temperatures ranging from -90°F to -290°F. The medium you should choose for cryo treatment should be liquid nitrogen. You need to ensure that you have introduced the metal to cryo treatment for about eight hours. For this, you can even soak the metal in liquid nitrogen overnight.

Eliminating Blemishes, Scaling, and Warps After Heat Treatment

To eliminate any of the blemishes that appear on the knife after the heat treatment process, you have to take the knife to the sander. At this point, it is especially important not to let your blade get hot on the grinder and ruin the heat treatment. Have a water drum near the grinder and dip the steel frequently. This way, if you feel that the knife is getting too hot, you can immediately dip it in the water to cool it.

But this time, there is a slight difference in how you approach the grinder. Usually, you hold the knife out horizontally and then grind away any of the materials still on the knife. This time, however, you are going to hold the knife vertically and then grind away.

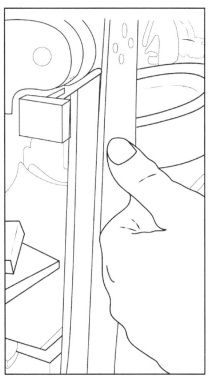

Figure 23: Vertical sanding is very effective in removing blemishes

One of the things that you will notice is that the sanding process might not remove some of the marks near the ricasso area.

For this, do not head back to the grinder again. If you can, take out the belt and use it manually to remove the blemishes and scaling. What you can do is use a long wooden stick. Tack one end of the belt onto one end of the wooden stick and the other end of the belt on the opposite end of the stick.

Bring the improvised belt to the knife and slowly sand away the remaining blemishes that you see.

Truing Your Knife

While most people assume that handheld blades are perfectly straight, the sad reality is that most blades are not straight. In fact, not only are most blades bent, but many are twisted as well.

So why are so many blades far from being straight? The answer lies in the fact that most people, knifemakers included, have not been taught to examine blades carefully.

Why is examining the blade important? This is because when you examine the blade, you get to check it for any defects or anomalies that you might have missed out earlier. Typically, when your blade is warped, then you might notice it easily. However, sometimes, you might have to check to make sure if there is a bend in your knife, especially when it might not be clear if there even exists a bend or not.

Here is how you do it.

Now we are going to use the idea of your dominant eye and non-dominant eye. Your dominant eye is the one you use to examine something. For example, if you want to peek at an object, then you often close one eye and open wide the other. The open eye is your dominant eye.

Let us start with the knife diagnosis.

To diagnose the straightness of a blade, hold the blade in such a way that the handle is furthest away from you. The edge of the knife should be towards the ground and the point aimed at your dominant eye. The non-dominant eye is closed. The back, or spine, of the knife should be in full view. Not only can the spine be examined for straightness this way, but straightness from the blade continuing to the end of the handle can be examined. Some blades are reasonably straight, only to slightly bend off somewhere along their bodies. Most will be bent one way or the other.

Sometimes, when you subject your knife to the heat treatment process, you might notice that it warps.

Warping happens for many reasons. Here are some of the causes for it:

- Heat treating of the blade is a delicate process. When you are subjecting it to all that heat, you might have to be careful how you distribute that heat. Sometimes, when bladesmiths use coal forge, they often forget to plunge the knife into the coal rather than simply place it on top of the distributed coals.
- During grinding, if cracks and splits are still present on the knife, then this can cause heated to be concentrated in certain areas, eventually causing the blade to warp.
- Make sure that you haven't skipped the tempering process or, for that matter, any process mentioned in the heat treatment of the blade. Remember that the only optional treatment is the cryo treatment. Everything else is important and should be followed in the steps mentioned above.
- Try and bring your metals as close to the non-magnetic limit as possible. This allows you to work with the metal better.
- Don't quench your knife in a sideways motion. Doing so will increase the chances of warping your knife.

Now let us assume that you have a warped knife. What can you do in this case? How can you straighten out the metal?

The process is fairly simple.

The first thing that you have to do is heat up the knife along the convex side of the curve. Once that is done, you can then hammer the knife or untwist it (or you can do both).

Let's look at each process.

Hammering

- When you are hammering, try to use the weight of your hammer to your advantage. If you find yourself holding on to your hammer with white knuckles, figure out how to get more comfortable.
- Find a rhythm and swing with your hammer instead of fighting against it. You can continue to hammer until you see the knife being straightened out. The index finger of the support hand is held at the exact

spot to locate the problem. The blade is lowered to the anvil or your workbench, the convex side of the bend facing up, without removing the fingertip from the blade.

- A quick visual check confirms the exact spot on the blade where the hammer will strike. As the dominant hand reaches for the hammer, the support hand breaks contact with the blade to hold the blade by the handle in preparation for the coming hammer blow.
- A more forceful blow follows one very light strike to confirm the accuracy of the technique.

The blade is reexamined for results and repeated if necessary. In this technique, the emphasis is on proper diagnosis rather than on hammering technique.

Untwisting

- You can also untwist the knife. The best way to accomplish this is by using clamps to hold the knife properly while you use the tongs to straighten the knife. This process works to remove the warp easily, but it might require more strength from your end.
- Another way you can untwist the knife is by holding the knife in a vise. You have to make sure that the portion of the blade that has incurred the bend is placed in the center of the vise (since that is the part that is going to get twisted). Clamp down on the vise as tightly as possible, this will put pressure on the knife, and begin to straighten.
- If the twist is too small for your hammer, then you can make use of a metal rod. Make sure that the rod is thin enough to work with the twist that you have. Place the knife between a vise and clamp it hard. Once you have done that, position the rod so that it is aimed at the twist. Using your hammer, strike the rod softly until you can untwist the knife.

CHAPTER 7: FINGER GUARD AND BOLSTER

Bolster

Making bolsters on full tang knives can seem daunting to the beginner. However, you can use the below process to make a bolster for your knife.

There are many materials that you can use to make bolsters. However, the recommended material for this purpose is brass. This allows you to make a bolster that is strong and sturdy and does the job well. Plus, it looks really good!

- When starting off, you will need to make markings for your bolster.
- Measuring allows you to focus your attention on the overall shape of the bolster and how you can work with it during the cutting phase. You can use a permanent marker to draw out the design on the brass piece. For the knife template that we have used, you can ideally go for a 1 inch to 1 1/2 inch bolster.

Figure 24: What your bolster pieces should look

- Then use your angle grinder or hacksaw and cut out the shape that you are aiming for.
- Now drill holes according to the template. If you have invested in a drill press, then you can make use of that as it provides you with more accuracy.
- When you are making a bolster, make sure that you don't use one single piece of brass. This will be difficult to add to the knife. Rather, find your design and create two pieces out of it. They can be clamped together on the knife. This makes it easier and you will be able to make adjustments easily if required.

- Once you have the 2-piece bolster ready, simply place one part of the bolster on the knife. Then place the other part on the other side of the knife.
- Once both pieces of the bolster have been lined up with the tang, it is time to use epoxy to glue them together.
- Smear the bolster pieces with epoxy and line up the pins with the holes in the tang.
- Push the bolster piece with the pins. Then hammer the pins through the tang and into the other bolster piece.

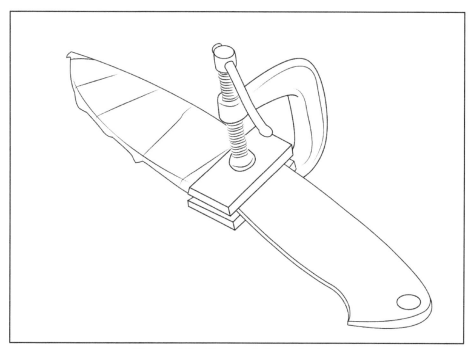

Figure 25: Clamped down bolster

- Now it's time to sand the bolster so that it flows perfectly with the tang.
- To sand it, simply use a 80-grit belt. Bring the bolster close to the belt sander and allow it to gently smoothen the part. Don't push the bolster too hard into the belt itself.

Finger Guard

There are numerous materials that you can use to make the finger guard. For our knife, we are going to use solid brass again. Make sure that the piece that you have with you is about 5 inches long and about 1 inch wide. If you can find a brass piece that is about ⅛ inches thick, then you have the perfect piece of metal to work with.

Time to get started with the process.

- Our first order of business is to mark the piece of metal with the outline of the guard. To do this, place the knife in such a way that the part where the blade of the knife begins falls on the piece of brass metal. This way, you have a part of the blade and a part of the tang on the brass piece of metal. Make sure that you place the knife as close to one end of the brass piece as possible. This allows you to use the other end of the brass as well. When you place the knife on one end of the brass piece, make sure you leave some space. About 1/2 inch of space is sufficient.

- This means that you have half an inch of space on one side of the knife. Measure a half-inch on the other side of the knife and mark that half-inch on the brass using a permanent marker. You now have a mark about 3-4 inches from one end of the brass piece (depending on the size of your knife).

- Now make two marks, one on either side of the tang. This is where the slot of the guard will go.

- Remove the knife.

- You will notice the lines you made for the tang won't extend across the knife. Take out your marker and extend both lines, so they cover the entire width of the knife.

- Once that is done, find the midpoint of these two tang lines. Draw a line that connects one midpoint to the other. Let us call this line the "midpoint line."

- Down use a drill press for the next step. You can also use your handheld drill, but you get more accuracy with a drill press. Clamp the piece of brass in a vise. Now, lower the drill press on one end of the midpoint line. Drill a hole.

- Move the piece of brass in such a way that the drill press extends the hold along the midpoint line. Eventually, the entire midpoint line will look like a gap that is almost the size of your tang.

- Once you are done, use a drill press to smooth out the gap as much as possible. When it is smooth, take it out and try and fit your tang through it. If you have the perfect fit, then your tang will go through the gap. If you don't, your tang might get stuck.

- If you would like to extend the hold slightly, do not use the drill press. Rather, use a narrow metal file to get the job done. Place the metal file on one end of the gap and run it back and forth a few times. Then do the same procedure for the other end of the gap. This way, you can extend the gap slightly. Remember that the guard should have a tight fit on the tang. It should not be loose, or the guard might come off.

- Once you have found out that the guard fits the knife snugly, you are then going to clean and polish the guard. To do this, you need to take a 600 grit sandpaper. Rub it on both sides of the guard. You need to rub it for a couple of minutes on one side and then the same duration on the other side.

- You can also use a grinder to complete the polish. You only need to subject the guard to the grinder for about 10 seconds or so to get the polish that you need.

- Once that is done, you can finish the guard by using any regular brake cleaner. Spray some of the cleaner on the guard and then wipe it off using a cloth.

CHAPTER 8: HANDLE

To make the handle for your blade, you will attach two pieces of material to the outside of your tang. These pieces are called scales. You can make your scales out of a wide variety of natural and man-made materials. While there are some benefits and drawbacks of using certain materials, a lot of this comes down to personal preference. When choosing the material for a knife handle, you should take into consideration the environment and the kind of abuse your handle will need to take. If you're going to be hammering on your handle frequently during the process of batoning, it might not make sense to use a softwood that could be easily damaged. Changes in temperature and humidity will also make some natural materials shrink and swell, which could affect the integrity of your handle.

TIP: Using a bolster will shorten the length of handle scales that you will need for your handle. Take account of that when making the handle design.

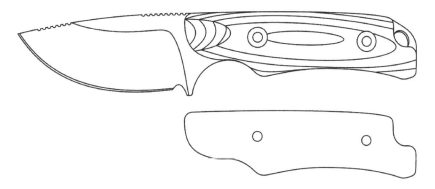

Figure 26: Handle scale template

Scale Material

Along with wood, one of the recommended knife handles you can use is made out of Micarta scales. Micarta is a form of synthetic material that is made out of certain kinds of fabrics, such as linen or canvas. They are usually soaked in resin. It is tough, lightweight, and makes a durable handle. When the handle is exposed to an oily or greasy liquid, however, it will make the Micarta a bit slippery. But that is a small drawback for an otherwise suitable material.

Another thing that you need to focus on is the pins that will be inserted into the tang and the handle. Pins are the pieces of thin, round metal that are inserted through holes to help hold the scales to a full-tang blade. These pins, once finished, will leave a small circle of metal visible on the handle. Pins can be made out of almost any kind of metal, depending on what you would like to see on your handle.

I would also recommend using Corby fasteners and Loveless bolts, if you have the taste for them.

Handle Making

- First step should be to shape the handle using the belt sander. In order to do this, you first choose the right material for the handle. You can either choose a piece of exotic wood with exquisite burls or use Micarta.

- You will now have a block of wood with you. The next step is to get the right dimensions for the handle.

- To get the right shape, you need to first understand that you actually need two pieces of blocks. These pieces will act as a clamp for your knife. To get the two pieces, you should use a hand saw to divide the block into two halves. You do this by running the saw straight down the middle of the handle. Try and make sure that the piece of material in front of you is evenly split in the middle. If you have uneven dimensions, then you might have trouble getting both halves of the material to form the right shape that you want.

- Each of the two halves should then be cut into the length of the handle. The handle length depends on the knife that you are making and the tang itself. But thankfully, we were prepared as we created a diagram to act as a blueprint for our knife. As we had seen earlier, the handle length that we are going to go with is 4 inches. However, try and cut it down to about 4 1/2 inches so that you can leave a little room for error.

- Once you have the correct lengths, you can then work on shaping the handle. If you have a rough idea for the handle, you can draw on the wood using a marker.

When you have the material for the handle (the scales) ready, you have to follow the below steps to complete making your own handle.

- Check to make sure your scales are perfectly flat. Figure out how you want your scales to sit on the blade.

- Make a mark on your scales to designate which side will be the inside. This will make it easier to keep track of which side to epoxy later on.

- Position one of your scales as it will sit on the blade. Clamp the blade and the scale together.

- Holding them secure, drill through the hole in your tang all the way through the scale.

- Push one of your pins through the holes, securing the two pieces. This will keep the existing holes lined up as you drill your second hole. Drill through the second hole in your tang, into the handle scale.

- If you have more than two pins in your handle, repeat this process, securing each new hole with a pin. Using your marker, trace the outline of your tang on the inside of the scale.

- Now remove all the pins and the scale that you just used.

- Use your hacksaw and follow the outline you made to cut out the rough shape of your handle. Put the scales back on the knife. It's okay if the scales are a little bigger than the tang. All you have to do to match them is sand down the profile of the handle to match the profile of the tang.

- Using coarse grit sandpaper, scratch the inside of your scales as well as the outside of your tang. Then, use acetone and a rag to wipe down all the surfaces of the scales. Next, we are going to mix the epoxy. One of the recommended epoxies that you can use is JB Weld. The ratio of epoxy to use will be 2:1. Which means you will mix two parts resin with one part hardener.

- Tape off the entire blade area of the knife, with some masking tape. You do not want to get epoxy on your blade.
- Using a clean and smooth stick, spread the epoxy all over the inside of each scale, and the tang. At this point, make sure you have enough epoxy that when you clamp the scales to the knife, the inside surface area is completely covered.
- Apply a little bit of epoxy on the ends of the pins. Put the pins through the first scale and into the tang. Fit the second scale from the other side. Make sure the pins go through the scale. Gently tap the pins with a hammer to make sure they don't get stuck and end up in the right position.

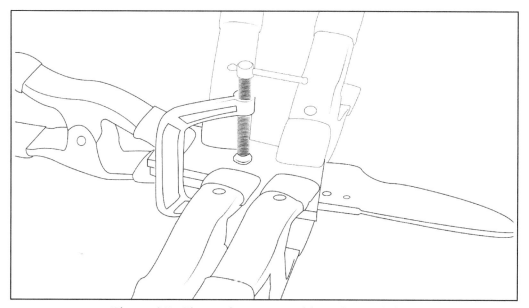

Figure 27: Clamp down everything nice and tight

- Clamp down on the handle, squeezing everything together securely. Wipe off any excess epoxy that runs out. Let your knife sit clamped overnight to dry.
- Once your epoxy has set, bring your knife back to the belt grinder. Clean up the edges and start shaping your handle.
- Test your grip as you go, take off more material wherever it puts pressure on your hand in an uncomfortable way.
- Once you're happy with your grip, take the belts down to a finer grit sandpaper. Finish up your handle by hand sanding with progressively finer grits until you get the finish you want.

Sanding and Shaping the Handle

Now that you have created the handle, you now have to get it shaped.

- Using the design on the wood as a guide, take your knife to the sander. For this purpose, you should use a sander with a belt that has 120-grit. With a 120-grit, you will be able to get the right shape and even add a smooth layer on your handle.

- Gently bring the handle to the sander. Work on the handle as you chip away the parts that lie outside the marked area. If you feel like you have to stop and examine the handle, do so.
- Continue working on the handle until you start seeing the shape that you had originally wanted to create. Work with the grit and then finish off the shape.
- Once you have done that, you might notice that the handle does not look 'finished.' It might have a rather rough body and plenty of wood shavings (if you are using wood) sticking out. At this point, you have to focus on giving a nice finish to the two pieces of the handle. Switch to 60 grit belt and then make your handle as smooth as much as possible.
- The next step into the sanding process is to make sure that you have sandpaper with the right grit.
- Before we even start the sanding process, you are going to have to protect your blade. Use a piece of leather to cover the blade. Make sure that the leather is soft inside so that it does not leave any marks on the blade. You can also make use of cloth, but the leather is tougher and resistant to sandpaper. If the cloth gets in the way of the sandpaper, then it might get messy with bits of stray cloth sticking to the sandpaper or revealing parts of the blade.
- Another reason for using a cover for the blade is to protect it from the vise. The clamps are going to hold the blade with the handle sticking out freely. In order to prevent any marks on the blade from the clamps, it is much better to wrap it using a cover (once again, preferably using leather).
- Now go ahead and clamp the blade and the handle ready for the sanding process.
- Start with an 80 grit sandpaper. When you are sanding the handle, you are going to move in a way that allows you to curve around it. This process allows you to cover the entire surface area of the handle.

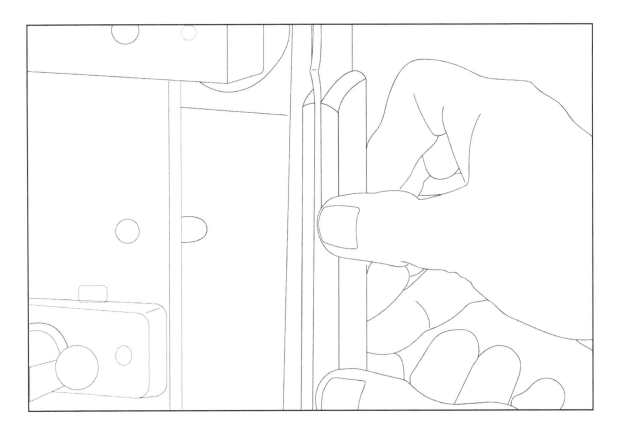

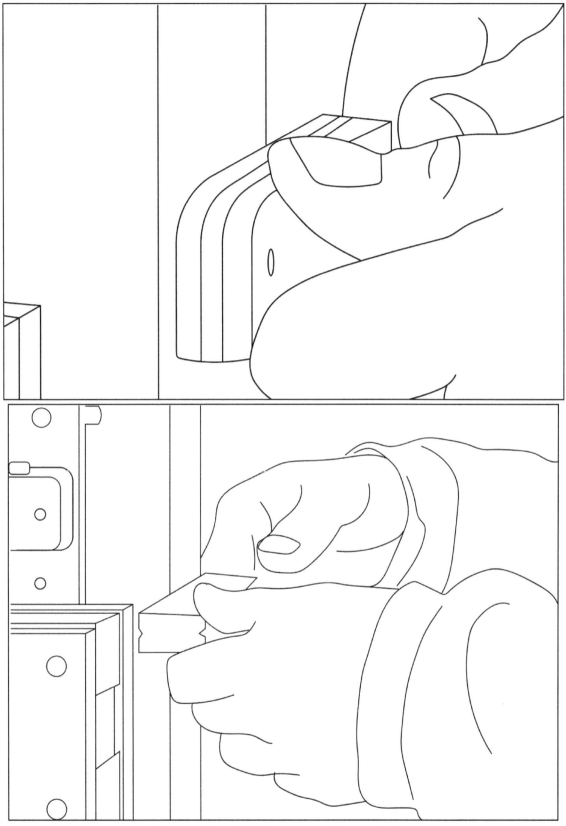

Figures 28 to 30: Proper sanding technique

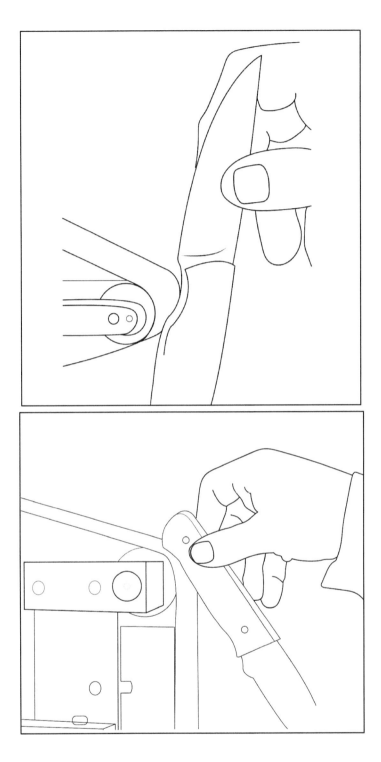

Figure 31 & 32: A small wheel attachment on a 2X72 grinder can be handy in shaping the curves of the handle

- Work with the 80 grit sandpaper for a couple of minutes on both sides of the handle.
- Once you have done that, shift the sandpaper to 240 grit.
- A few things to remember during the sanding process:
  - Take a little extra time when you are sanding the pins. If you don't spend enough time, they might 'dome' out a bit. What this means is that they bulge out of their holes because the area around them is getting sanded faster than them.

- o Be careful when you are sanding near the areas that have metal. If you sand those areas too much, then the metal will start protruding out, just like in the case with the pins.
- o After you have completed sanding using the 240 grit sandpaper, examine the handle and see if the results are according to your expectations. If you have to, redo the sanding process to get better results for your handle.
- Once the handle is fully ready, use Danish oil to polish and coat the entire handle.

CHAPTER 8: THE FINAL PROCESSES

Hand Satin Finishing for the Knife

- We had earlier worked on the handle, and this time, we are going to work on the blade. For finishing this knife, we are going to do a hand satin finish. We will basically replace deep scratches with finer ones, till the scratches are so fine that they aren't visible. If you want to sell your knife, then finishing it is necessary for your customer to feel good about his purchase.

- The best way to work with the knife is first clamping down a piece of board between a vise (make sure the board is narrow and more or less reaches the width of the knife blade). Then place the knife on top of the board and clamp the knife over there.

- Alternatively, cover the tang or handle of the knife with leather and then clamp the handle, leaving the blade projecting outward for you to work with your sandpaper.

- Use a little bit of WD40 and rub it along the blade. This elevates the sandpaper's cuts, and makes it last longer.

- Apply the WD40 on the belly of the knife. Whenever you are ready, take the sandpaper and place it on the blade that you are planning to finish. Then start moving the sandpaper along the length of the knife.

- You are going to sand the knife starting with an 80 grit sandpaper. Then continue using progressively higher grits as you remove scratches from the coarser sand paper.

- Remember that when you are using sandpaper, you want to work at an angle. Imagine the knife is pointed away from you. You start with the tip of the knife and move the sandpaper side-to-side as you make your way up the knife's blade, towards yourself.

- Rather than directly sanding the paper from left to right, you can adjust the sandpaper to be at an angle. So when you move from side-to-side, it looks like the sandpaper is positioned at a roughly 45° angle. This allows you to cover more surface area while you are sanding.

- Sand both sides of the knife using the above process. Once you have finished sanding, then you can work on the bevels. When you start working on the bevels, start by covering them with a blue marker. This allows you to check if there are any spots on the bevel. In case of spots, you should levelling should be done. Use a machined bar and dry paper to get the job done.

- Remember that the primary purpose of sanding is to remove any small scratch marks that might have appeared on the blade. In the end, when you have finished the sanding process, go over and check your work. Make sure that you are satisfied with the results. If you notice that there are still scratch marks, then take out the sandpaper and start working on it again.

- Don't be afraid to take time to remove the scratches. At this point, many knifemakers feel frustrated because they are so close to the end. They progress through the sanding process quickly to shoot through to the end. However, you should take your time. The fact that you are so close to finishing your knife might compel you to speed up the sanding process, but you should take your time with it.

- Using a progression of grits for sanding will fetch you better results than jumping grit sizes.

- When you have done everything right, you should be left with a hand satin finish.

Sharpening Your Knife

When you are working on the sharpening of your knife, you will come to realize that there are many sharpening tools out there in the market. Let us look at some of the tools that you can use for your sharpening process.

Understanding More About Knife Sharpening

The thinness of an edge makes it the most vulnerable part of your knife. This is also the part of the blade that takes the most beating. Every knife requires edge maintenance eventually, as even the best steel wears with time. The basic mechanics of sharpening remain the same, whether it's your blade's first edge or its hundredth.

Some grinds do best with a small, secondary bevel on the very edge. Other grinds, such as the Scandi grind, are sharpened by refining the original grind. This makes the Scandi grind a very easy grind to sharpen for beginner, as the angle needed is easy to determine.

Make sure you have good lighting before you start the sharpening process. As with grinding, your sharpening process involves starting with coarse grit and slowly moving down to finer and finer grits.

When sharpening, the key is to match the angle of the knife's edge to the sharpener. By keeping this angle consistent and moving your edge across finer and finer grits, you'll remove all the metal that won't make up the edge of your blade. The mechanics behind sharpening aren't difficult to understand, but good results take a skilled hand and refined attention to detail.

Knife Sharpening Technique

- Hold your knife flat on its side on your coarse stone. Lift the spine slightly so that the edge is resting on the stone at a sharp angle. Ideally, you should keep an angle of about 20-25°. However, you can choose the angle that works best for your knife.

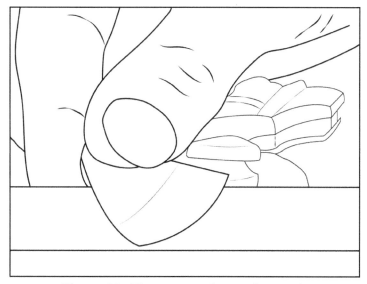

Figure 33: The correct sharpening angle

- Additionally, try and use a 1,000 grit stone in the beginning. This stone works well for beginners.
- Move the edge across the stone lightly, as if you were trying to slice off a very thin piece of it. Make sure the entire length of the blade, from the heel to the tip, comes in contact with the stone. Always sharpen your blade in the direction away from you. Repeat this process several times, maintaining the same angle.
- As you remove steel from the edge, a tiny burr will eventually form on the opposite side of the edge. The burr is a rough, raised metal curl that results from grinding metal. The burr should appear evenly along the entire length of the edge. If you find that it is absent in an area on your edge, you aren't sharpening as much on that particular spot.
- Once you have a burr along the entire edge, switch sides. Repeat the process until you have a burr on the second side. If you have any chips in your blade, you'll have to continue grinding with a coarse stone until all the steel is removed past that chip. Once you have set your edge with the coarse stone, move to a finer grit stone and repeat the whole process.
- Use a 'strop' method to remove the final burr on the blade's edge. Stropping involves the same motion that is used while sharpening on stone, but in reverse. Instead of cutting forward, the blade is drawn back, dragging the edge. Use light pressure and make several passes, alternating sides. Stropping makes sure that the sharpness of your blade remains for a long time. Note that stropping stones are different from sharpening stones, and you should invest in one if you are serious about knifemaking.

TIP: Here is an important tip to remember while sharpening your knife. Make sure that you clean your knife before you bring it to the stone or strop block that you are using. If you don't, there are chances that you might contaminate the stone that you are working on more.

Testing the Edge

There are many ways to test your edge to see if it is sharp enough. Everyone has their own favorite method, from seeing how well the blade cuts through the paper to carefully drawing the edge along a fingernail. In my opinion, the best way to test the edge is to use it. The efficiency at which it completes any given task helps to determine whether or not the edge was sharpened properly.

Another method to test out the edge (especially for our hunting knife) is to run the knife through a paper towel. If you can drag the knife through the towel without much resistance and by its own, then you have yourself a well-made and sharp knife.

BONUS CHAPTER: MAKING TONGS

Now we are going to focus on making simple, but effective tongs that you can use in your metal works.

There are numerous materials that you can use for making your tongs. One of the more common materials that you can get your hands on is rebar. You can get one that is about 3 feet long and is about 1/2 thick.

- The first thing that you have to do is find the center of the bar. The make a mark on the bar using a permanent marker. From the center, measure 3 inches to the right and then 3 inches to the left. Call these two points A1 and A2.
- Now make an indent on A1 and A2. You can do this by placing the bar on the edge of your anvil and lightly tapping it. Using only the two indentations, you have a space of 6 inches in the center.
- Now take the rebar to your forge and heat the marked part.
- Bring over the bar back to the anvil and flatten the heated part. Strike on it using your hammer and make sure the entire 6 inches of the center is getting flatter. When they seem flat enough while still having about an inch or so of thickness, take the part back to the forge and heat it.
- Whenever you heat the bar, make sure that you are heating it to the yellow range temperature.
- Once the bar has been heated, bring it back to the anvil. Now we are going to use the horn part of the anvil (the little protrusion at the front). Place the heated part on the horn and then start striking the bar to bend it in such a manner, the two ends of the bar are going to meet. Strike the bar evenly so that when you create your tongs, you don't receive an uneven or awkward shape.
- Eventually, you are aiming to bring the two ends to a point where they look like they are making a 'U' shape. When you have achieved the shape, you have completed the first part of the process.
- Heat up one end of the bar and bring it to the yellow range temperature. Head over to the clamp and hold it firmly with the end pointing upwards. Now we are going to use a chisel and place it in the center of the base of the bar. Essentially, we are going to split the end. Line up the chisel in the center and strike it using a hammer. You can make the split as deep as possible but make sure that you do not overdo it.
- Repeat the above process on the other end of the bar as well. Basically heat it, clamp with the end pointing upwards and strike it so that you split it.
- The next step is going to involve the ends as well. This time, heat the ends and using the horn of the anvil, bend them inwards at a 90-degree angle.
- Start with one end of the bar and then work on the other end. In the end, you have both bars bending inwards. This formation becomes the hands of the tongs, holding any piece of material between them.
- Go back to the center of the bar. Heat it again and bring it back to the yellow temperature range. Remember those indentations that you had made? Choose a point slightly close to those indentations and strike the bar so that it starts bending inwards.
- Do the same with the other side of the bar as well.
- Now it looks like you have an indentation on both sides of the bar, close to where it bends to create the 'U' shape.
- When you have done that, you now have a very rudimentary form of tongs. You can use the bent ends to clamp down on any piece of metal and then bring it out of the forge easily.

- One tip for the process is to replace the rebar with coil springs because coil springs have that extra bit of elasticity to allow you to squeeze the two ends of the bar together.
- When you are using coil springs, make sure that you first start by cutting 3 feet of metal off the spring. Once done, you should then straighten the metal. Straightening a coil spring is relatively easy as the metal itself does not provide much resistance. Heat the parts that are bent and using a hammer, strike the metal lightly until it straightens.
- You can make use of many other metals for this, but rebar is easy to get while a coil spring makes for effective and flexible tongs.

CONCLUSION

Bladesmithing is a satisfying process. The hard work that you put into it reaps some incredible results. Of course, it all depends on the efforts and the time you put into it.

Do not worry about the mistakes that you make. Every mistake is a learning curve for you. It is for this reason that the metals you are using in this book are easy to work with. Even if you do not get the right shape or perform a mistake during the grinding process, you don't have to worry about the metal. You can either choose to correct it easily or get yourself the metal (as it is fairly easy to get).

There really is something special about a razor-sharp knife that, once experienced, will be hard to live without. The superior cutting performance also factors in blade shape and geometry and ease of sharpening.

Do go through this book carefully before you jump in on the heat treatment processes. Make sure you understand the concepts. Most importantly, be careful when you are working with metals.

Always put yourself first. Are you in a safe environment? Are you keeping yourself protected? Are you staying a safe distance from fire and other harmful objects?

Remember, there is no point in trying something when you are not feeling safe.

Another factor that you must consider is that bladesmithing is a fairly time-consuming process. When you are aware of this, you might decide how best to approach the various processes. That is why, make sure that you are comfortable with one process before you carry on to the next. For example, if you feel like you are not doing the quenching right, then refer to this book and try again. Try not to skip to another step if you haven't properly performed the previous step.

You might find yourself physically exerting force on the metals you are working with. Sometimes, this might become a little uncomfortable. Rest your hands if you think that you are putting too much strain than is absolutely necessary. However, remember that if you follow the instructions in this book, then you won't have to strike the metal too hard.

Simply watching your blade come to life is one of the most enjoyable sensations you can experience. I am sincerely hoping that you have such an exquisite feeling yourself.

Keep yourself protected and enjoy a wonderful bladesmithing process.

And if you feel like it, drop a quick review for this book as well. I would really appreciate it.

REFERENCES

Blandford, P. (2006). *Blacksmithing projects*. Mineola, N.Y.: Dover Publications.

Blandford, P. (2010). Practical blacksmithing and Metalworking. New York: TAB.

Parkinson, P. (2001). *The Artist Blacksmith*. Crowood Press.

Streeter, D. (2008). *Professional Smithing*. Lakeville, Minnesota: Astragal Press.

INTERMEDIATE GUIDE TO BLADESMITHING
MAKE KNIVES, SWORDS AND FORGE DAMASCUS

WES SANDER

INTRODUCTION

Before We Begin

Firstly, ask yourself, "Why do I want to make a sword or knife?"

The next question should be, "What do I plan to *do* with the knife or sword?"

Now, that question may be perceived as strange by most people. Why should I make a knife when the market is filled with a lot of low prices, yet very attractive blades, for sale?

I've been asked this question a number of times from quite a lot of people. Some people are okay with a small knife that can be carried in their pocket to use in cleaning their fingernails or opening an envelope, etc.

Others want a knife that can be used in hunting for cutting up game after a successful catch. Some see the knife as an important tool, one to always care for and not be without. These people desire a knife that can last for a lifetime, and that will hold an edge.

A large number of people who make knives, or are thinking of making knives, are doing so because they are not satisfied with the knives available in the market, and making one is the only way they can get their desire.

Knives and swords reek of adventure, gallantry, swashbuckling, and gallantry. Their creation is full of myth and mystery.

I am presenting techniques and guidelines for making knives, swords, and Damascus steel with this book. You can utilize this book to make one or numerous knives or swords, or it can be used as a handbook to start up a workshop and eventually earn a living with the craft.

Let me make a suggestion that you first read the whole book from cover to cover as though it were a novel. Once you are acquainted with the whole range of consideration, you can start to realize your knife-making goals in a step-by-step manner.

Let's get right into it!

CHAPTER 1: COMPREHENSIVE GUIDE TO KNIFE MAKING

Despite the fact that we use knives daily, at least in the kitchen, have you ever thought if it would be possible for the people of early civilization to survive without a knife? Today, various types of knives are used, such as pocket knives, camper and hunting knives, paper knives, bread knives, etc. A knife made of flint was a source of food and was used to provide shelter in the olden days. Some people say the invention of the wheel was the greatest invention to have happened, but how was the wheel built without cutting equipment? The first hand-making equipment that was used to control the world around us was the knife.

Different materials are used to make knives. Earlier, it was bronze, flint, and copper, then lastly, it was steel. With the modern equipment used in knife making, the methods for making knives have also advanced.

Folding knives and knives with fixed blades still exist. So what has really changed over the years? The materials are what have changed the most! Recently, we use sophisticated materials to make knives, such as titanium, steel ceramics, or carbon.

Hundreds of years later, a knife became more than an object for plant cultivation and more than a weapon for hunting animals. We use a knife every day because it has found its way to our tables. Knife making became a real art. Knife engraving, adding gemstones and customization are now common.

Every knife that you make can be a real stunner and a show stopper. It will astonish you of the magnificence and the distinctness of the knives you make. They are elegant and sleek, and you can create each with your own touch. An advantage of making your personal knife is that you can choose the steel that meets your prerequisites.

What can we call a Good Knife?

Before going any further, we have to go back and take a look at the entire concept of people and knives. Just as with other things, there must be the same number of value structures and attitudes as regards knives as there are people. This chapter can therefore only be of the utmost value if you make use of the information in it as it suits your desire.

Of course, knives can be anything from an exquisite work of art to an item in a shoddy dime-store to a powerful weapon or tool. How amazing a knife is, is solely dependent upon the user's value for it.

A knife's value to you is based on how good it satisfies your desire. You may like a knife that you bought ten years ago so much that its quality hasn't waned. On the other hand, you may dislike a "good" knife that is quite heavy to carry or doesn't hold an edge as much as you desire. Or you might just prefer a cutting-edge, corrosion-resistant, high-performance, computer-age model over a simple knife with an old wooden handle. And, apparently, another knife lover could just love it the other way around.

The fact of the matter is that you are the ultimate judge, either as the user or knifemaker.

Design

It's not enough to say that a knife should look fantastic and feel comfortable to you, it should also be strong enough and not overly heavy. "Overweight" is one of the most annoying faults of most knives, especially those designed to be carried in a sheath or in the pocket.

The knife's design should be such that the flow, of weight, mass, and lines, as well as the material's physical strength and the edge's keenness, should all work together as an energy "transmitter," from the user's hand to the cutting edge. The knife's design is a physical expression of the purpose it was intended for.

Knife-Making Steel

We need to explain some things about the materials you are going to use before we proceed to knife-making equipment. You should focus on many things when choosing a knife making steel, especially if it's going to be your first time making a knife.

Knife makers use several kinds of steel. You should know some basic information about those that are majorly used. Depending on how you make knives, either by forging or stock removal, there are a number of steel types to choose from.

All steel needs to be treated with heat. As a starter, you might not have a heating oven yet, so go for something simple, something you can easily heat-treat and work with. Stainless steel, carbon steel, and tools steel are the commonly used steel in knife making. There are plenty of steel comparisons on the internet that will help you choose. The following are the steels most commonly found in knife blades.

O1 steel: It is perfect for beginners. It is very tough, oil quenched, easy to work with, wear-resistant, and holds an edge perfectly. It needs to be taken care of to prevent rust.

1084: It is also good for beginner knife makers. It is good for uncertain heat-treating. It can be purchased anywhere. It does not need to be soaked for long.

1075: It is the same as above and quite affordable. It allows heat treatment with a blowtorch (not so high temperature for heat treatment, 830 degrees or thereabouts). This makes it a perfect choice for beginners.

1095: Percentage of carbon is high (95 percent), and it is mostly used for making knives by forging. In my opinion, it is the best knife making steel.

Stainless steel: It is more expensive. The blade will not rust, so there is no need for maintenance. There might be a need for someone to heat-treat it for you. It sharpens easily.

Top Tools for in Making Knives

If you are just starting and you don't intend to take knife making serious, do not waste too much money on the equipment. Buy equipment that is not expensive and is important. Simple equipment is required for simple projects. If you decide to make a knife using the stock removal method, this means all the gear used when working with fire (big hammers oil and anvils) are not needed.

Tool #1: File

This is the favorite equipment of many bladesmiths—good old-fashioned file. Great things can be done with this simple equipment (of course, except drilling a hole). Files are the first equipment you need to get, and they are not expensive at all. Smoothing, grinding, finishing—all can be done with files that come in various shapes and various grit sizes. Many people made their first blades out of an old file. Files can be bought at every metal shop, and they cost no more than $10. You still need to have a set of files in your garage, though there is a lot of power equipment that can replace the files and do the job much faster. They also require manual to work.

Tool #2: Clamps

When you are working, you need something to hold the knife. So buy several pairs of clamps; you will need them. They are cheap, so try to buy various kinds if possible. You can get C-clamps and welders for starters, then progress to bar clamps, one-handed clamps, pipe clamps, and so on. You can purchase them online at Home Depot at $10 or more depending on the type.

Tool #3: The Hacksaw

Also, an important piece of equipment with a high-quality blade is the hacksaw, which is needed especially in the steel-cutting and steel-shaping process. The hacksaw is always needed to start the knife-making process. The job can be done faster with power equipment, but they can't be used in tight corners. You can order a hacksaw at Amazon starting at $20 and make sure spare-blade kit is ordered as well.

Tool #4: The Bench Vise

Everyone who deals with metal requires one bench vise at least. When buying a bench vise, there are a lot of options to choose from, so simply start with the one that enables you to change the orientation of your work: a 360-degree swivel base adjustment. A good bench vise can be found for $100, but you can buy a used one if you feel that is expensive. An all-around bench vise size is generally five inches, but you can opt for something much bigger.

Jaw caps should be mentioned when we talk of a bench vise. They are designed for the protection of your knife. They are normally made of rubber, plastic, leather, aluminum, or copper; and they can go for around $20 on eBay.

Tool #5: Grinding Abrasives

When it comes to polishing a blade, fine grinding and finishing works, Cones, sandpaper, rubber abrasive wheels, points, and sticks are all put to use. If you're a knife maker and you want to give a unique final touch to your work, then a rubber abrasive is a *must-have*.

Tool #6: Drill

A drill press is very convenient, and it is a better choice, while hand drill with some bits for drilling steel is very good for a beginner knife maker. You can consider buying a used drill press with a drill vise. It will save you time by improving your accuracy. A hand drill can be bought for about $30. A ten-inch drill press at Sears costs around $121. A set of Cobalt drill bits costs around $30 on eBay. A four-inch drill press vise costs $17, and it will get the job done very fine.

Tool #7: Sharpening Stone

In the knife-making process, the last step is sharpening. When it comes to buying a sharpening stone, there are numerous options to choose from. The price ranges between $20 and $200, even higher sometimes. A lot of brands, stone sizes, grit textures, and stone shapes exist in the market, and the material of the stone is a determinant factor for the price. Most times, knife makers make use of diamond sharpening stones, but you can try water stones, Arkansas stone, ceramic stones, or whatever suits you.

Tool #8: Safety Gear

When grinding, cutting metals, and heat-treating steel, make sure you always use safety equipment: dust masks or respirators, gloves, and safety glasses. Serious injuries can be prevented by safety equipment; it can also protect your hands, eyes, and lungs from heated metal hazard dust particles. Gloves and glasses are very cheap, and instead of a dusk mask, a respirator is always a better solution. A high-quality 3M respirator can be gotten at Home Depot for $100.

A fire extinguisher is required for knife makers who make knives by forging steel. A five-pound rechargeable fire extinguisher doesn't cost up to $50. This is a small investment you can make to prevent fire outbreak at your workplace.

Tool #9: Dremel or Another Rotary Tool

Another tool is Dremel. Although it's not an important piece of equipment, it can be used in cutting materials, cleaning rust, grinding details, jeweling, or customizing with mounted abrasive cones, cut-off wheels or small rubber, points, and bits. For most knife makers, Dremel 400 is the first choice, and you can find it online for $77. You can check eBay to find the best offer. You can buy a flex shaft attachment or a handpiece along with a Dremel, which is a very convenient accessory since the motor unit won't have to be held in your hand.

More Advanced Pieces of Equipment

You will need one of the aforementioned equipment at a time or the other. People who want to do knife making for leisure can invest less than $1,000 and have a very good basis. Although you might have to invest more if you are in between, moving from doing knife making leisurely to being a full-time knife maker. In case you're looking at becoming an expert at knife making, discussed below is the equipment you will need to have in your garage or shop.

Tool #10: Belt Grinder

We are talking about 2"×72" industrial knife belt sender made for professionals, not the small bench belt grinders. Purchasing a smaller 1"×42" (belt dimensions) belt grinder shouldn't be a choice here. If the equipment is too expensive for you presently, don't buy it yet. Do not purchase a grinder that won't get the job done.

Belt grinder prices vary a lot depending on many factors—motor speed (variable speed control is a fantastic option to have), wheel speed, wheel size (usually eight inches, though you can find any dimension you want), motor power (if you intend to grind long steel bars and tick, don't go 1 HP), accessories, body material, tracking adjustments, ability to quickly change belt (quick-release mechanism), and so on. There are similar specifications in all professional and powerful belt grinders.

An affordable belt grinder for knife making, including shipping, costs about $600. High-end models can even be as high as $3,000. Check the internet to find a used one that's still in a good condition.

Tool #11: Heat-Treating Oven

As said earlier, steel has to be given heat treatment. In the knife-making process, heat treating is the most essential, and demanding shops that sell steel usually offer heat-treating services also, so heat treatment can be outsourced. However, you'll need to own a heat-treating oven (some call them kilns or heat-treating furnaces) if you want to take knife making serious.

You can surely use a torch to heat a two-inch stainless-steel blade, but trying to heat a five-inch or a longer blade at the constant temperature of 1,000 degrees can be quite complicated. While the other parts of the blade remain cool, you can have the correct temperature at the center of a blade. One of the reasons you should buy a treat oven is because irregularity in hardness can lead to failure as blade simply won't hold the edge.

When you want to purchase a heat-treating furnace, what is the most essential thing to know? The oven's major function is to heat the blade to an accurate high temperature and to maintain a constant temperature. This means it must have a manual or digital temperature controls and a dependable temperature controller. The capacity of an oven depends on the blade you want to heat. The maximum temperature it can attain is also essential, and the temperature standards are 2,000 °F and 2,350 °F.

The oven is an expensive piece of equipment, and its price depends on its size. An oven that has a chamber size of 6.5" W × 4.25" H × 18" D costs about $1,200.

You should also buy industrial stainless-steel foil and ceramic racks. You will need a heat-treating foil to protect the blades and prevent them from discoloration and scaling; you will also need a rack to position the blades in the oven.

Note that heat-treating ovens are mostly electric, and they use up a lot of electricity.

Pro Tip: Tool #12

Pizza? No. Beer? No. AC/DC soundtrack to enjoy while grinding? No.

Tool #12 is YouTube, Instagram, or some other social media network! Publicize your work, your current project, and have a great time. Seek opinions and advice. Like or follow other knife makers. Endeavor to learn something different, something new. Copy some ideas and improve on them. Share your knowledge, learn some new knife-making skills, and find out about new tools. Give valuable information to people who are in need of new handle materials, searching for heat-treating services, or probably just need assistance selecting the best steel for their project.

As you work, record videos and upload them on YouTube to help people pick up new ideas from you. Join a community of large knife makers and have a positive influence on upcoming and already-existing knife makers.

Step-by-Step Guide
Step #1: Sketch the Knife

In getting started with making a knife, sketch the design and shape of the blade on the paper. Ensure that you keep it at a scale size of 1:1 for easy construction. The dimension of the blade is dependent on your choice. However, large knives require a lot of steel and can be heavy.

Step #2: Choose Tools and Knife-Making Steel

You should stay away from stainless steel because it has to be subzero-tempered and isn't a good choice for making good blades. An excellent knife-making steel is the 1/8-inch-thick carbon steel (01). It is a good choice for producing blades because it is easy for drenching.

When making handles, wood materials are a perfect choice. Although you can use any material you want to make the handle, the materials that you can combine with rivets are G10, micarta, and kirinite when making the full-tang knife. These materials are the best to make knives because they are waterproof.

Use a permanent marker to trace the blade onto the slab. This will serve as a guide when cutting the steel. Ensure to trace the tang accurately specifically because the blade and the tang are connected as one piece.

You can use a hacksaw, bandsaw, vise, an angle grinder with cutoff wheel, drill, grinder, and safety wear.

Step #3: Cutting the Steel

Cut a rectangle around the traced blade using a hacksaw. This is to separate it from the main slab. To cut a thicker steel, make use of a stiffer hacksaw, then grind the rectangle down to ensure it forms the blade profile.

Put the rough-cut blade in a vise and grind out excess steel. Follow the guidelines when molding the profile. Complete the blade shape using the grinder. Then use the grinding wheels to softly grind the edge into a slope. Make this slope on both sides of the blade to get the desired blade edge.

Afterward, use a drill bit of similar size as the rivets you want to use. Place the holes in the tang. You may need a different number of holes depending on the size of the blade.

Sand the blade at this point with sandpaper or finer grits. Ensure you sand every surface of the blade, including every scratch. This is to help improve the blade's shine and quality.

Step #4: Heat-Treating the Blade

The perfect way is to use a forge in heating the blade. A forge is a type of brick- or mud-lined fireplace used to heat metals. A gas or coal forge can be used for this procedure. A torch can be used for smaller blades. A torch is a thick stick with materials burning on it; it is used as a source of light.

At this stage, the blade is ready for quench hardening. Quench hardening is a mechanical process for hardening and strengthening of steel. To cool the blade, you must douse it in a hardening bath, usually a bucket of motor oil. Immerse the entire blade in the bucket.

Leave the steel in the fire until it gets an orange glow. Place it close to a magnet to be sure it is sufficiently hot. Once the steel attains its optimum temp, it loses its magnetic properties. If it doesn't stick to it, let it cool sufficiently at ambient temperature.

This can be repeated three times. On the fourth time, do not cool the steel in air; rather, dip it in oil. This requires extra care because there will be fire eruption when the blade is dipped into oil; therefore, cover the exposed parts of the body using personal safety gadgets. When the blade is hardened, it could break easily if it is dropped; thus, handle carefully.

At this point, set the oven (thermal chamber used for heating) at 420° Celsius. The blade should be placed on the center rack and heated up for sixty minutes. Once the 60 minutes is over, the heat procedure is finished.

As before, sand the blade with smoother grits of paper and clean the blade for some extra shine.

Step #5: Making a Knife Handle

There are two sections of a handle for a full-tang knife, one on each side. The wooden piece should be cut using a hacksaw while the pieces are sand in simultaneously to ensure that the two sides are symmetrical.

Once that is done, drill the holes on each side for bolts. Attach a vise and let it dry overnight. A saw is needed for finished products and handle modification. Insert the bolts, leave about 0.125 inches, and peen them using a ball-peen hammer. Then you can file them down. Bear in mind that you must also sand the handles.

Step #6 Blade Sharpening

You will need a large sharpening stone for this process. Pour sharpening oil on the jagged side of the stone. Then bevel the blade at an angle of 20 degrees from the zone of the sharpening stone. Move the blade against the stone in a cutting movement.

The handle should be drawn up while moving the blade to sharpen from bottom to the top. After a couple of moves, switch the blade over to the other side. When you have made a sharp edge on all sides of the blade, take it to a fine stone.

Step #7: Try Out the Knife

Cut a few pieces of paper with the knife. A well-sharpened blade should easily cut the paper into strips. Once the knife performs well, congratulations! You've got your DIY knife.

CHAPTER 2: COMPREHENSIVE GUIDE TO SWORD-MAKING

Have you ever thought of making your own sword? I don't simply mean a knife or blade. I mean a real, full-working, and harmful sword. Most of the sword makers use old techniques sharpened by the ages. However, some techniques are more recent. You will learn a couple of new things during in this section.

Caution: The making of a sword is quite easy for someone acquainted with their hands, yet it takes patience and requires full concentration. The task ahead is daunting, and you would need to invest hours thinking, wandering, and endeavoring to solve the next stage the most ideal way. In any case, with this section, it becomes easier, and anyone can make a sword in a significantly auspicious way.

Also, most steps along the line can be done in other ways depending on the alternative tools you have.

Step 1: Materials

Full blacksmithing tools comprising of the following:

Required tools: forge, tongs, hammer, and anvil

Shaping tools: bench grinder, belt grinder, angle grinder, and cutting torch

Steel-finishing tools: belt grinder, angle grinder, belt sander, drill bits, drill squeeze, wire wheel, a variety of sandpaper, and steel files

Woodworking tools: drawknife, saw, files, table/hand sandpaper, linseed oil, and multifunction knife

Optional yet recommended: induction heater, power hammer, and air hammer

Be cautious. Ensure you're skilled with each of the tools you use.

Step 2: Dreaming and Designing

At the initial stage, you need to understand what you need your sword to look like once completed. It is imperative to have a good plan before commencing. Keeping the design simple makes the work much easier and better. Stick to a straightforward geometric design rather than complex fantasy-like thoughts. At first, sketch a design on paper and try it out on cardboard or something stronger.

Gathering ideas from history is a smart idea. Carry out some research on what they actually look like in the past. See what current swordsmiths are producing too.

Step 3: Finding the Steel

This is a crucial aspect. The steel used for a sword is really important. The use of high-carbon steels is strongly recommended. Few steels can be hardened. Unless you only plan on having the piece as a beautification, you need to choose a decent piece of steel.

You can determine what sort of steel it is, depending on the sparkles produced. High-carbon steel will produce sparkle that splits off into a few branches.

If you don't have a forge, then you need to make one. If not, get a piece of steel that is almost the same size as the sword and move past the forging process.

Step 4: Starting Off

To start forging, get the steel to the correct size and shape. Cut off the extra parts of the piece if the tip of the steel tapers is more than you need. It's better to cut the opposite side before the hole in the steel.

If you have the right length, simply cut the tip for the tang. Use a cutting torch to cut the sides off. You could make it about ten inches in length.

Now that you have your right steel measure, it is time for the fire!

Step 5: Shaping into "Your" Blade

If the size of the blade is different from your ideal blade style (i.e., the blade is excessively wide and not sufficiently long), you should decrease the width of the piece. This all can be carried out by hand, but a power hammer might probably be needed depending on the steel's mass.

Heat the whole section with a burner gas forge till you see a yellow glow. With the hammer, carefully apply blows continuously along the piece length.

After a few heats, it will start to increase in length and thickness while it decreases in width. In the process, the sides of the steel will start to thicken up more than the center. To balance this, start hammering it on the blade's flat side.

The entire procedure requires a lot of forward and backward movement. By using hand tools, it is a lot less demanding with limited damage possibility.

The general goal is to extend the blade by compressing the width and reducing the resulting thickness.

Change to a pneumatic hammer for better work. Hit the two sides of the blade to make it appear more like a sword.

Once the appropriate width, length, and thickness are attained, start squaring up the piece as a whole. The aim is to get the sides parallel, fit in the bends at the tip, and attain a uniform thickness of the blade.

Now, the blade has its actual appearance and is set for the next step.

Step 6: Grinding the Appropriate Profile

When you've accomplished a uniform thickness on the steel, the following stage involves grinding it to the ideal proportion.

The initial step is to imagine what you need the blade to look like. Ensure the regions you mark out have thick-enough steel. Include this in the planning procedure. You should make certain that the blade has enough material.

Commence profiling with an angle grinder using a thin cutoff plate. Get so close to the real shape without damaging the blade. It is better to leave abundant material and do the finishing with a grinder.

You can design the tang in different ways, yet it has to follow the simple idea of curving the two sides with a tapering tang.

Once you've used the angle grinder, finish up the profile either using a belt grinder/sander, a bench grinder, or an angle grinder with a grinding wheel.

Before grinding, all the slag on the steel must be removed because it dulls the belts rapidly.

To remove the surface slag, a variety of things can be used:

- wire cup on an angle grinder
- flap sander on an angle grinder
- wire wheel on a bench grinder

The use of a wire wheel is recommended except it could turn out to be way too strong. If that is the situation, then use the cup brush or the flap disc. Try to just remove only the slag and secure the steel.

Step 7: Making the Bevels

At last, the steel now takes the form of a sword. The next challenge is to determine what you want the cross section of your blade to look like.

The cross-section determines what the blade would look like if it were to be cut in bilaterally on the blade's perpendicular axis.

The primary concern when preparing your cross section is to consider the sort of grind you need. The three major types of grind are flat, concave, and convex. These grinds all have their own technique, advantages, and disadvantages.

- Flat grinds are straightforward as they sound. The grind is an angle across the whole blade's surface. It is blunter than a concave grind because it has more material. This grind can be efficiently sharpened in the "field." Though it is a strong style, it is not the hardest.
- Concave grinds bend inward toward the cutting edge. They are the sharpest of all grinds, with the best cutting edge. However, they also have the weakest edge. Such factors should be put into consideration. The concave grind is the hardest of all grinds to make.
- Convex grinds are generally found on axes. The edges curve smoothly. This provides the blade with the best strength of the three grinds. However, a convex grind will give you the bluntest edge with the lowest cutting force. This style is considered the least demanding to cut.

The other part of the cross section is the fuller, sometimes inaccurately called a blood groove. The fuller gives a lighter weight without sacrificing quality and strength. Its properties are almost the same as that of a construction I-shaft.

You may decide to go with the convex grind if you can't maintain consistency across such a wide surface. Try not to make any fullers if the blade you made is way too thin.

At the start of the grind, first, ensure the blade is well hammered and ground perfectly flat. If you are satisfied with it, you can move on to a bench grinder or belt grinder. Begin by slicing off material at about an angle of 45 degrees. Make the grinds using a dull belt, then gradually move up to a sharp one. If you begin with a sharp belt on a corner, the belt will dull rapidly.

Cutting bevels involves going gradually at a time. Allow the machine to do the work. Take your time while working on any project. This stage will take a while. Utilize the unsupported portion of the belts. Consistent pressure should be applied at the same angle. Start from the shallow ends. Afterward, let the machine work its way to the center of the steel's thickness. Cut the bevels to the same proportion from both sides till less than about 1/16 of an inch is remaining.

Step 8: Heat Treatment

This is the most important step. This transforms a sharpened shard of metal into a splendid weapon. If you have no idea what kind of metal it is, oil is the safe choice to use. Quenching in water can make certain steels crack, and this is the reason for it to be avoided.

Steel quenching hardens steel because it transforms carbon molecules into a tight lattice arrangement by quickly cooling in something like oil after they are heated up. The steel needs to attain its optimum temperature, which can differ depending on what sort of steel you have. Again, the convenient step is to simply go past the magnetic point of the steel.

When heating the piece up, be careful not to overheat it. Begin with a low temperature and gradually raise it. Ensure to evenly heat the blade, concentrating on the tip and edges. The tang is not a vital point, but its joint is.

Use a piece of three-inch PVC pipe to hold the oil, then glue the end cap on and clamp it to a firm table. Ensure the section of pipe is a bit longer than the sword. Ensure the oil is warm before quenching. This can be accomplished effectively by heating up a piece of metal to orange and placing it in the oil as this will help warm up the oil.

When the blade is uniformly heated and the oil is set to quench the blade, dip the blade into the oil and forcefully swirl it at the same time. This ensures an even cool-off. Allow about 30 seconds for the blade to stay in the oil, followed by air cooling. When cooled, transfer it to a very high grit belt to quickly eliminate the scales.

Tempering comes after quenching. The quenching makes the steel fragile, and tempering brings back the sturdiness of the metal. Both the tempering and pre-quench temperature, as well as time and liquid type, will be determined by the type of metal. Evaluate what you have so as to find the best possible way.

Step 9: Blade Finalization

This stage is all up to the maker's choice. You could choose to use a Scotch-Brite belt to clean it up.

First, get the blade to the desired shape with 60–80 grit. Then move to 120 grit. Ensure that all the deep belt scratches are eliminated with each increase of grit. Keep on expanding the grit to 220. Then 400 if you wish.

Once you've removed all the deep scratches with the 120, most bladesmiths will move to hand-sanding. The process takes a while, but the outcome is worth it. Go on to the following grit, perhaps 220. Repeat the procedure and sand until only the 220 grit sandpaper scratches are left. Sand simply with a little piece and pressure by hand. You can decide to wrap a piece around a wood block. Another choice is to use an orbital sander. Be cautious though. Apply moderate speeds and dull paper. Be cautious of the sword edge. When sanding one side, apply more pressure so the sharp edge is pressed to the table and can't cut your finger as you sand. Next, move to 400 grit, then 800, 1,200, and possibly 2,000. The general principle is to double the number as you go up.

Patience is important.

Step 10: Pommel Creation

Another important part of the sword is the cross guard and pommel. These can be made out of bronze or brass.

The role of the pommel of a sword is to balance the weight of the sword and to aid in the mobility of the weapon. Without it, the sword will be very stressful to wield. The importance of a pommel cannot be overemphasized as its usefulness is backed by history.

Get the metal from a pool heat store. Pools use crude synthetic chemicals, so the metal must have the capacity to withstand corrosion; therefore, they use materials like copper or brass. To plan for the melting, clean the muck off the pieces after some time, with lots of hitting and smashing.

Use a crucible with a gas burner in a forge in melting. Preheat the pieces at the top of the forge, not inside. The aim of this is to aid in the melting and to remove more of the impurities from the metal. Every time the piece melts down, clean off the slag from the top and add another. As soon as the crucible is full, it is time to pour.

Empty this into a section of pipe. Place the pipe into some sand kept in a bucket and do the pouring. The leftover material could be made into a mold for bars for melting ease later. Allow time for it to cool and cut out the piece from its pipe.

If you have an appropriately sized piece to begin with, you could skip this prior steps for the pommel. Any pommel design can be accepted. Numerous options exist out there. Put the piece on a lathe after you have obtained your "stock" piece.

The pommel aids in holding the whole sword together. After some time, weld some threaded rod onto the tang, which then runs through a hole in the pommel. This is the initial step. Place a drill bit on the lathe (the rod's size) and drill it through the pommel. Afterward, drill a hole for the nut to join the rod to the pommel so it could be concealed. A regular drill should be used to get a large portion of the material out, followed by an end bit to ensure it is square on the bottom side. With that, proceed to the cross guard.

Step 11: Cross Guard

The cross guard has a couple of vital functions. Firstly, prevention of an enemy's sword from sliding down your blade into your hand. In the absence of this, a blade will clash, slice, and cling. The other vital part is to prevent your own hand from going up into the blade, which is not likely to happen but possible.

Any material can be used for this, just like it is with the pommel. A piece of bronze, brass, steel, titanium, aluminum, etc. could be used. Anything can be utilized. You can take any design with it also. Square or rounded is great. Hello, be creative. Anything can be used. Create a dragon. Okay back to the real world.

Get a piece of material, brass or bronze. Their alloys can be extremely challenging to work with. If it gets excessively hot, the material will disintegrate like a failing sandcastle. Some individuals use the term *red short* to describe the phenomenon. Also, the material has the tendency to work-harden, implying that by bending and working it, it gets more difficult to move. It must, therefore, be strengthened by gradual heating and cooling. It tends to crack along failure points even if it doesn't disintegrate. Working it cold is simply the solution to this. To smash it into shape, power hammer should be used. This is the most recommended from experience.

Once you have a piece that's large enough, drill some holes in it to allow the tang to go through, and file it to make it clean. It must be sized so that it lay flush with an appropriate slot in the piece, then set a bar through it. The bar will at that point set into the vertical milling machine vise. You will be able to make its sides totally parallel with the tang's whole/line. After that is accomplished, go to the grinder to clean the piece. The same way of cleaning and wire wheel as before.

Connect it to the sword by soldering it with unadulterated lead solder and flux. Ensure you fill in every one of the gaps for strength.

Step 12: Wooden Handle

The wooden handle is next. For the tang to go through, the handle has to have a hole. This is done specifically with both drilling and burning. A straight hole is set for the tang by the drill, making a lesser material needs to be burned. Afterward, a mock tang is built to burn a size almost the same. Any extra space after cleaning is done will be filled with epoxy when it is glued. Now for the exact procedure.

The initial step was the drilling of the hole. Try not to burn out the hole, because it is quite difficult and may end up unsuccessful. The best way to go is to drill a hole. Place the piece in the vertical milling machine and drill a hole smaller in size than the tang width. A drill press can also be used just as effectively by hand, needing a larger stock piece, and leaving room for more error. Begin with a typical length drill bit. After the small-sized bit, utilize a longer one that can now fit in the machine and can be set into the wood due to the hole. You could drill the remaining by hand if you are still not fine with the hole piece after that.

With the hole now drilled, proceed to the grinder and clean off all the corners, rounding the piece. With it more cylindrical, place it into a lathe and begin to shape the piece. After sizing down, sand the lathe. With the handle now finished, it's time to do the pommel connection.

Step 13: Pommel Connection

Add some threaded rod to the back to connect the pommel to the sword. Get the right-sized bolt to go through the pommel and cut the head off, leaving you with threads. After this, cut a groove in the thread to slide onto the tang.

You now have the wooden handle's size. So to match, cut the tang of the sword. Weld the rod on and try to slide the handle on too. Grind the weld down if it is too big. After this, slide the wooden handle on, followed by the pommel. If you observe that the handle didn't line up square with the cross guard and pommel, shape the top and base of the handle to match.

If the connection satisfies you, slide it all together and place a nut and washer into the pommel.

Step 14: Gluing

After all the pieces have been prepared, all that is left to do is to glue them into a full sword. A two-part epoxy should be used as a bonding agent.

With everything arranged, mix the glue. Every part needs glue. Slather it throughout the tang and pour into the wooden handle. Also, line the top and base of the handle. The handle should be slid onto the tang and the pommel. Slide on the washer and crank the nut down.

Leave the glue to dry and get cured for several hours.

Step 15: Polishing/Buffing

Buff the sword using the glue set. An angle grinder with a fabric wheel and a buffing compound should be used. Clean the whole cross guard, pommel, and sword blade. Before wrapping it in leather, sand the handle and apply linseed oil.

Step 16: Leather Wrap

Should you not really like the way the wood turned out, wrap the sword's handle. This step isn't compulsory though.

Firstly, locate a section of leather that conveniently has the correct length. Wrap it around the handle and take note of the spot on the top and base of the wood of the leather by marking it. Draw a demarcation just between the marks and cut it with scissors.

For stitching, punching is first required because leather is extremely tough. Before punching, mark the spots where you have to punch. A fork could be used to press down to make the mark. Do this till you've marked all the points. From the sides, ensure the marks are about an eighth of an inch.

Using only a punch and a hammer, punch the holes on a scrap piece of wood. An awl could also be used. Drilling with a very small drill bit is another common technique for thick leather. Punch all of the holes, and then it's ready for stitching.

Begin the stitching process from the handle top by looping it underneath. Ensure it is tied at that point and wrapped over. Stitch it in a similar pattern down the handle. Rethread the line repeatedly through the same spot at the base to ensure that it stays.

Using two needles beginning at the top and acting like you're tying a shoe is a better approach to this. It can be finished using a knot at the end.

Step 17: It Is Done

There you have it finished. A step-by-step guide to making a sword. Well, now, sharpening is all that is left. Use a file or high-grit sander or sharpening stones and so on to sharpen it.

CHAPTER 3: BLADE-MAKING STEEL

Steel is made up of iron and carbon. All steels consist of other elements in limited amounts, including manganese, phosphorus, silicon, and sulfur. Steel is referred to as carbon steel if it doesn't contain any of these elements. Steel used for blades of knives are increased with extra elements and are referred to as alloy steels. These additions give unique properties for various kinds of steel. Alloy steels containing these additions are resistant to corrosion and labeled stainless steel, and when it comes to making knife blades, they're the most frequently used steels.

A well-built knife is a tool that functions consistently well without failing. Nevertheless, producing a knife that is not liable to fail can be a challenging task to accomplish, because you must sharpen a knife blade to a fine edge that must not dull or fracture. If you desire to achieve this, it is important to pick the right knife material as the wrong steel and grade will ultimately result in premature failure and edge dulling. Metals for knives are not all made in the same way. Below is a list of the best kind of steels for knife making.

Best Steel for Knives
Tool Steel

For knife production, tool steel is one of the most regular options. Generally, tool steels are carbon steels that incorporate additional alloying elements that boost their mechanical qualities. These alloying elements often raise the steel's resistance to corrosion too, however not to the level of stainless steel.

A standard tool steel grade that is utilized as a knife material is A2 (5 percent chrome, 1 percent carbon, air-hardening tool steel), which has excellent toughness, although can't range hardness to the level of some other tool steels.

Still, if not well taken care of, A2 could be susceptible to rust. Another solution that has higher resistance to corrosion and edge retention than A2 is D2 (high chromium, high-carbon, air-hardening tool steel). However, this solution gives a lower toughness. A top tool steel that is best at retaining a knife edge is M2 (molybdenum based), but when it comes to specific demands, it can be too fragile.

Carbon Steel

Steel grades with a high carbon quantity are attractive for knife making because they give the blade hardness and strength needed to hold up against impact and wear. However, the right heat treating must be achieved on high-carbon steels. If a quench is used too rapidly, the knife will be excessively fragile and may fracture. If the metal is normalized or strengthened, it'll be excessively soft, and the blade's edge won't be sharp for long.

Knives made from carbon steel can be inclined to rusting as well. This is due to the fact that carbon steel doesn't consist of many alloying elements that help to guard it against corrosion. It is necessary to ensure that a carbon steel blade does not rust.

Common grades of carbon steel for knife making consists C1090 (wear-resistance high-carbon steel), C1075 (high-carbon steel), and C1045 (medium-carbon steel).

Stainless Steel

This is the most frequently used type of knife-making steel, and it is the perfect steel for resistant-free knives. The additional advantage of using stainless steel is the chromium and other alloying elements inclusion that boost resistance to corrosion. Typically, stainless-steel knives are formed out of martensitic or austenitic stainless steels.

If you require a knife that has the appropriate edge retention, the ferritic and martensitic grades of stainless steel must have a sufficiently high-carbon grade, enough to achieve high hardness. Categories like 440 (high-carbon steel with the highest hardness and resistance to wear) and 420 (high carbon steel with at least 12 percent of chromium) have been commonly used in making knives.

The austenitic grades, such as 316 (standard molybdenum-bearing), is another stainless steel that may sometimes be utilized in making knives. Still, austenitic grades are typically incapable of hardening satisfactorily to give a lasting edge. Low carbon types of austenitic stainless steel, like 304L (extra-low carbon stainless steel), shouldn't be used when making knives, except resistance to corrosion is more important than the life of the blade.

Steel Properties

Choosing steel for specific knife making demands is based on the metal's properties and other aspects like manufacturability. If the metal is difficult to manufacture, then it is useless in a manufacturing environment. These properties are a result of the alloys included in the steel and by the techniques used in its manufacture.

Here are the ten most basic features of blade steel:

1. **Hardness**: A steel's standard and ability to resist sustained deformation. It is measured on a Rockwell scale (hardness scale dependent on indentation hardness of a material).
2. **Hardenability**: Steel's ability to be hardened by the process of heat treatment.
3. **Strength**: Steel's ability to endure applied power.
4. **Elasticity**: The ability of steel to flex or bend without breaking.
5. **Sharpness**: The blade's initial sharpness, functionality, and usability.
6. **Toughness**: The steel's strength to absorb force before the breaking
7. **Edge holding**: The steel blade's ability to keep an edge with no repeated resharpening.
8. **Wear resistance**: The steel's resistance to corrosion and wear all through use.
9. **Corrosion resistance**: The ability of the steel to resist degeneration that may be caused by reaction with its surrounding.
10. **Productivity**: The simplicity and ease at which steel is machined, cold-formed, forged, extruded, blanked, and heat-treated.

Nomenclature of the Steel

The knife's classification, type of steel, and properties are often derived from the internal metal structure. Steel's internal structure suffer changes because it is heated and cooled. The systems based all through these changes are names such as Martensite and Austenite. Martensite is a stable structure that can be made by the rapid cooling of specific kinds of steel throughout the heat-treatment process. Metals capable of forming Martensite are commonly called martensitic steels, and this type of steel is common with the cutlery industry.

Additions for Alloy

By adding extra elements to the metal throughout the process of melting, the properties of steel can be changed. The alloying elements that are vital to knife production have been explained below these lines with short information on their effect on steel properties.

- **Carbon**: It appears in plain carbon steels, so it isn't an alloying element.
- **Chromium**: It's the main element in martensitic stainless steels commonly been used for cutlery utensils. It increases hardenability, resistance to corrosion, and resistance to wear.
- **Molybdenum**: It increases elastic strength, hardenability, and resistance to corrosion, particularly pitting.
- **Nickel**: It increases hardenability, toughness, and resistance to corrosion. It's one of the leading elements in austenitic stainless steel used occasionally in making dive knives.
- **Vanadium**: It increases hardenability and develops fine grains. The structure of grain in steel is a significant aspect of strength and wear resistance.

1095 Knife Steel

The primary form of carbon steel and the most commonly used in the creation of various types of knives is the 1095 steel. It contains 95 percent carbon, which reduces the measure of wear that a blade will encounter during its lifespan and enhances steel hardness.

Despite the reduction in wear caused by the high presence of carbon, the presence of the trace amount of manganese in 1095 steel makes it not as hardened as other steel types. Although manganese in higher concentrations causes steel hardening, it causes the blade to be more fragile.

1095 Steel Usage

The 1095 knife-making steel is extremely easy to sharpen and keeps an appropriate knife edge. But it tends to rust quickly because of its properties. These blade types will typically have some type of coating to resist rusting, but if the edge has been rightly preserved, rust should not be a major issue for you.

This steel is good for blades that aren't much thin because the steel is more brittle than other steel types. It's plain to sharpen; however, if a knife made with this type of steel doesn't have an appropriate measure of thickness in it, it can easily break. For this reason, it isn't the best grade of steel for sushi knives, folding knives, or tools.

It can be made to undergo heat treatment to increase its strength completely, but steel can end up fragile after this, breaking in the process. Although 1095 steel can be effectively utilized for chopping knives, it isn't the best option. Truly, it shines; however, there are more steels out there that are more appropriate for that application.

This type of steel is very suitable for polishing, although it hasn't been alloyed with stainless steel.

Characteristics

It can be used in producing replicate swords and daggers or blades. The military also makes use of it in their functional show swords. Not only is 1095 a major type of steel used in making dining tools, but it's also a more useful stainless appliance than the ones used in making swords. The 1095 steel is also a major steel used for rituals and in some religious ceremonies. Some kinds of machetes are also made from the 1095 steel.

Oils are essential in the maintenance of the 1095 knife. After every use, rinse and wipe clean, and oil it once every ten days. This gives the knife a polished look, and the oil also creates a barrier that hinders moisture from reaching the steel.

CHAPTER 4: COMPREHENSIVE GUIDE TO FORGING DAMASCUS

Damascus is an old method of craftsmanship that evolved from India in 300 BC. It started as a medieval culture in the western regions. Damascus steel has been proven to be exceptionally good and seemingly strange, capturing the hearts of many users. The art and craft of Damascus was a productive one and was made popular by the name of the region it emerged from. However, Damascus gained a flourishing industry in the area of weaponry as a result of the Arabians introducing Wootz steel into the city of Syria in Damascus.

Wootz steel was imported from Persia and Sri Lanka into Damascus for the production and utilization of hybrid steel blades. These hybrid steel blades have a characteristic feature of hardness and toughness. This technological evolution was clearly born out of intellectual minds who understood the resultant effect of merging various metals to create weapons of increased tensile strength over those made of pure steel. The unique trait of the Damascus steel is in its ability to captivate the mind yet remain mysterious although it is not pure.

The material has characteristics and features of multiple bands and molting welded together in a pattern-like model to make decorative blades of different shapes and length without easy annihilation. No record exists till today to prove the identification of alloys/intermixtures in original Damascus steel. Although in present-day Damascus steel making, the practice of merging pure metals is used with differences in relation to personal preference and needs.

Iron stands out in its use by metalworkers because of its carbide-enhanced solidity and grit, although the metalworkers have a wide range of choice to combine materials to make steel billets. According to the history of Damascus steel, early references were reported missing around AD 1700, leading to an inscrutable reputation for Damascus; however, this resulted in the downfall of patterned swords that later put a halt to production fifty years afterward. The booming industry that exists today has constantly put to remembrance the significance of the ancient tradition of the Damascus steel.

Steel Composition

Metallurgy and chemistry are the fundamental basis for the alloy/composition and the various applications in steel production and utilization. The ingenuity and technicality of Damascus techniques and processes are directly linked to the sciences behind Damascus steel and steel making. Due to the durability and longevity attributed to the former reference, the Damascus steel was referred to as the superplastic, not because it was not a real metal and it was never pure. Various types of modern steel have exceeded the Damascus blades in terms of efficiency; moreover, the blades produced recently have been extremely rigid and effective due to its native chemical composition. Different steel types welded together to form billets have been used in the production of modern Damascus steel blades since 1973. These billets constitute strips of iron that aid firmness on a molecular basis. This enables flexibility in layering them out according to the needs indicated by specific utilization of the blade and preferences of the blade owner. Damascus steel blades are custom-made to suit individual preferences; they are not produced in a rigid like pattern.

It involves a simple process:

Steel ingots are formed into billets. The billets make a sandwich-like fold pattern in other metal types. The product formed is made up of a series of layers in hundreds or more with good varied design and solid density. The steel has a high level of integrity and uniqueness as a result of this tested process.

Ductility and brittleness are two major dichotomous structural types that make up the fundamental composition of the Damascus steel. Ductility aids compression of the material in order to absorb high levels of energy that helps to reduce failure in the integrity and efficiency of the blade. Brittleness, however, relates to feebleness, which is highly misleading.

Brittleness refers to the flexibility of the material in the prevention of breakage, also in enhancing edge sharpness. The Damascus blade has an advantage of durability and easy cutting due to this structural process. The convex grind provides sharpness to the thinness of the edge so that sliced material yields to the sides during the stroke and thus reduces "sticking" that often occurs with blades having blunter edges. The convex grind is aided by the structural brittleness.

During the process of forging, malleability and sustained strength are acquired due to the formation of carbon nanotubes in the steel. High performance, efficiency, and strong quality in steel integrity are ensured by a high concentration of carbon. This is the sole reason why carbon is essential in the development of Damascus steel blades. During the process of forging, small steel ingots slowly form into a preferred shape of a blade. This causes the iron carbides to align into bands that form distinct patterns. These patterns evoke feelings in the Wootz steel from ancient India, and they portray old aesthetics and style of production. Metalworkers today are able to replicate much in the same order in which Damascus steel was known to exist centuries ago.

Heating and Finishing

The distinct details of the Damascus steel vary according to individual preferences and choices and also on the type of metals being merged together. Below are the lists to the general heating and finishing processes for preparing Damascus steel. A fixed temperature between 1,500 °F and 2,000 °F is used in the heating treatment of the steel in relation to the banding and a combination of austenite and cementite.

- Fix the temperature of the furnace according to specifications.
- Place the metal block in the furnace. Heat through its cycle to its initial temperature.
- After heating, cool steel by soaking for ten minutes.
- After quenching steel in oil, transfer to liquid nitrogen for 60 minutes.
- Steel tempering involves subjecting the steel to heat and cold in order to make it strong and hard. This process must be carried out twice.

Steps in the subsequent finishing treatment:

- Apply a grit finish to the blade.
- Etch in 50/50 diluted solution of ferric chloride and distilled water without pre-buffing. Leave the blade in solution for at least ten minutes.
- Remove the blade and rinse under running water.
- Repeat the process at five-minute intervals till you get your preferred result.

- To neutralize finish, immerse blade in tri-sodium phosphate.

Making of the Damascus Blade

Prior knowledge of heating and finishing, the Damascus steel is highly needed in the making of the blade as shown in the process discussed below. Therefore, a metal maker needs a detailed knowledge of both processes in order for him to complete the process below. It's an essential order for specifications, and the process works together.

The process of making the Damascus is simple and easy; however, it must be done painstakingly and with caution. Also, it's a time-consuming process that ensures real aesthetics and the development of a well-balanced, productive blade.

1. Glass and leaves materials are added together in a crucible. These help to prevent oxidation.
2. Heat crucible to melt the materials together.
3. At the cooling temperature of the crucible, carefully remove the metal ingots and heat them to a specific temperature required of forging. This stage entails "sandwiching" of the process described above. The metal is hammered while it is still very hot. After metal completely cools, reheat the metal to forge again. This cycle is repeated to sharpen edges and shape the blade.
4. Cut the blade and hand-forge the final details after the final shape is achieved.
5. Shave away the excess carburized metal from the surface of the blade.
6. Insert grooves and drill holes into the blade surface as needed or desired.
7. Hammer blade flat again by reheating. Polish to set the blade's near-final form.
8. Etch the surface of the blade with acid to accentuate the pattern.
9. After completion, clean acid thoroughly from the surface of the blade.

Damascus Knives

There are various types of Damascus steel knives, and they are used for a wide range of purposes—for example, in wood cutting, hunting, camping, and so on. The reason for use and the type of knife determine the composites that are merged together to make a Damascus knife.

Examples of some common types are listed below:

- Flip-flop knives
- Hunting knives
- Carving knives
- Serrated knives
- Rigging knives

A unique and distinct feature of any type of Damascus knife is in its endurance—that is its ability to endure force of any kind applied to it. In addition to the enduring force, it also has a long lifespan.

The aesthetics and high efficiency of the Damascus steel knives are its most common aspects; however, lovers of the knives see it as the perfect example. There is an absolute distinction between two Damascus knives as no two knives ever look the same. Damascus knives have fashionable patterns engraved by metalworkers into the blade during the forging process. Each knife is unique and priceless as an expression of art. In view of its mysteriousness and special quality, the Damascus style will undoubtedly last longer in the years to come. Even after two thousand years, the tradition and style are waxing stronger.

CHAPTER 5: LOST WAX CASTING

In lost wax casting, the wax pattern is melted in the process of molding, and it's an old-fashioned technique. Hence, the name lost wax was given to the process. The attracting force of the lost wax to various foundrymen and artists lies in the integrity and dependableness of the method. This process also enhances the formation of elaborate sculptures, ornaments, and automobiles. Despite the fact that the name of the process has been changed to investment casting and several other names, the method still maintains its luster and glow.

Lost Wax Casting Process

In the ancient times, hands were used in making the lost wax casting for every single piece of mold. However, in the modern world, one pattern can be made into a series of patterns, although the pattern is melted or lost during the process. Hollow patterns or solid can be used for molding purposes

There are two major ways of making the pattern: direct method, which involves directly making the wax, and indirect method, which is by sculpting the model in claylike materials and then making a wax copy out of it. The molten wax is then poured into the mold to the required thickness or consistency and turned upside down to cool. In order to give a flawless finishing, the wax pattern is carefully removed from the mold and improved upon after cooling the wax. Spurs and gates of wax are joined together for pouring the molten metal after the wax pattern is ready. When the pattern is wet, materials enclosing the pattern will hold it firmly in shape. A grainier material is added to make a solid mold in which the metal can be poured, and it then solidifies.

The mold in the kiln is heated till the wax liquefies. Mold placed in the kiln is fixed in place with flasks. A vacuum is then formed in the cavity where the wax existed. The molten metal, like bronze or gold, takes its place. The mold is detached after the metal cools in order to extract the cast.

Applications of Lost Wax Casting

- It is used in the casting of necklaces, earrings, and other small parts. Brooches and buckles are clothing accessories that are also made from the lost wax casting process.
- In the making of engine blocks by automobile producers, a method known as the lost foam is often applied. In recent times, the lost wax process has been often used in several other areas, like dental restoration, fine jewelry, and sculptures. Silver, gold, aluminum, brass, or bronze are cast with this method.

Merits of Lost Wax Casting

Flexibility of material:

- Any material liable to burning, evaporation, or melting can be used with the lost wax process to create a mold cavity.
- It also replicates the fine details of the initial wax.
- It provides shapes of casting that would be difficult in other methods.

CHAPTER 6: JAPANESE BLADE

The art and craft of forging a Japanese sword is a meticulous and cautious process, which has improved over the years both in stylistic and aesthetic considerations, as well as improvements in technicality. For the absolute beauty and flawless finish of these blades, the smith should have certain qualities, which include finesse, patience, and a detailed eye for the beauty of the materials, as well as the limitations.

Tamahagane was often used by the Japanese smiths in ancient times. The tamahagane was a kind of steel made in a Tatara shelter from iron-rich sand. Although modern-day smiths still use this type of steel, the ancient manner of making swords by the Japanese is now made in the last functional Tatara shelter located in Yokota, Shimane Prefecture.

Although the Tatara smelting process is highly efficient, it still has some disadvantages which include the following:

1. High concentration of impurities
2. Lack of consistent dispersal of carbon content, which is a vital tool for converting iron into steel

When there is a high concentration of carbon, the metal will be fragile, and when there is a lower concentration of carbon, the metal will be too soft.

Kitae: Forging the Blade

The folding technique of kitae was majorly developed in the bid to correct and balance up for the quality of the tamahagane. The smith will firstly choose good pieces of tamahagane and forge weld them into a single block. This single layer of block forms the outer part of the finished blade. After that, the smith begins to hammer out and fold the block back on itself. This is a very strenuous process. There are two main resultant effects of this process:

1. There is a standardization of the carbon throughout the metal and the extraction of impurities out of the steel. With a great wealth of experience, a smith can direct with precision the quality of the steel in this way.
2. The folding results in the patterns that have made these blades popular all over the world. Layers are formed every time the block is hammered and folded backward. A 14-time fold produces 16,000 layers. The surface in between the edge and ridgeline now concisely shows texture in the *ji* when the blade is finished. By contrasting the direction of the folding, the smith has a choice to choose any specific texture he wants, such as *ayasugi-hada* (concentrically curved grain) (2001.574) or a *masame* (a straight grain parallel to the edge). He can also fold the block continually in the same direction in alternate directions or crosswise. Each method results in a unique fashion of texture.

The *kawagane* is the outer skin that envelopes a softer core, or *shingane*. This combination enhances the flexibility and the strength of the blade to withstand breakage under stress. The harder *kawagane* also suits sharpening than the more ductile core. The two layers are heated and hammered out into a long bar. This welds the layers together and forms the blank from which the finished sword is made. After the blade has been forged into its fundamental form. The smith uses files and planes to bring out a final shape after a rough polish.

At this junction, we can accurately pinpoint the distinguishable features of the sword, which includes a clearly defined profile, point, and ridgelines, as well as the tang and a smooth level surface.

Yaki-Ire: Hardening the Edge

The most complex and significant aspect of the sword-making process is the hardening of the edge. The super quality sharpness of the blade is as a result of effective hardening of the edge.

The blade is firstly coated in a mixture of water, clay, ash, and other ingredients. This mixture is known as *yakibatsuchi*. Every smith has his own unique recipe, which is often hidden from others. The smith then spreads the yakibatsuchi systematically over the surface, creating a thicker texture along the spine and a thinner texture at the edge. The smith meticulously heats the blade while working in a forge room without light, except the light emanating from the glowing of his coals.

Crystal structures in the metal undergo changes as the temperature increases. The smith carefully observes the color of the glowing blade, and when the high temperature is reached, the sword is quickly dipped in a trough of water.

Steel structure changes to austenite at the critical temperature, around 750 °C, a phase where carbon and iron combine completely. When the blade is rapidly cooled by quenching, austenite becomes martensite, which is the hardest kind of steel.

Where the thick yakibatsuchi was applied, however, the blade will slowly cool down, transforming into ferrite and pearlite instead of martensite. These are softer and more flexible. The combination of softer body and hard edge is what gives the blade its desirable qualities, just like the *kawagane* and *shingane*.

Also, the hardening of the edge makes an obvious change in the metal's surface. A variety of effects can be produced depending on the manner in which the clay mixture was applied. This edge design is known as the *hamon*, and it is one of the most vital aspects in the blade's aesthetic appearance. Every one of these patterns has a specific name. For instance, *sanbon-sugi* is a zigzag line in clusters of three while *suguha* portrays a very straight hamon.

Following the edge's hardening, if the smith is happy with the blade's quality and appearance, it is then passed to the polisher, who then gives the blade a last mirror-like polish, and other craftsmen, who will then make the sword mountings and scabbard.

Complete mountings (36.120.417,418) have numerous elements, including metalwork like *tsuba* (36.120.79) and *menuki*, wrapping, lacquered wood, silk cords, and ray-skin grips. Though all these are pieces of art in themselves, the blade is the only true centerpiece of the completed work, an instance of the ingenuity that has been shown by Japanese smiths for centuries and their desire to accomplish the ideal blend of art and technology.

CHAPTER 7: GUIDE TO BUILDING A SIMPLE FORGE

There's one thing you have to face if you desire to work with metals—heat is needed. With the availability of heat, you can make any metal, no matter how tough, submit to your will. You'll never gain complete mastery over this stubborn material without heat. However, it isn't difficult to finally make the decision to take another step toward teaching yourself this smithing skill.

You'd learn how to build an effective but simple forge in this section. With this forge, you can heat steel hot enough to the temperature needed to effortlessly shape it.

Step 1: Materials

Some rocks, like granite, a bucket of mud, and an iron or steel pipe, are required for building a forge. Due to the fact that heating galvanized metal is bad, do not give consideration to galvanized pipes. However, coating the pipe in some layers of mud and using the forge outside for proper ventilation can be used to counter it.

Step 2: Construction

Place the rocks in a ring. You can create it any size you desire, but it is preferable to keep it small so as to get maximum heat.

After this, you need to use a thick layer of mud to coat the inside of the forge. Coating with mud will prevent the ground from absorbing the heat. The rocks are also insulated by the mud so they don't crack.

Step 3: First Firing

To get the fire sufficiently hot, the metal pipe should be connected to a vacuum cleaner on blow. Some steel can be heated to test how hot it gets and then melted in the can.

Step 4: It Gets Hot!

The forge at this point reaches forging temperatures able to melt steel.

Step 5: Conclusion

The forge can be upgraded a bit and made bigger.

CHAPTER 8: ARRANGING THE SHOP

Make your tools and shop neat with a place created for each thing. Take proper care of your tools and plan your shop arrangement.

Arrange your tools so that they are all in a tight little row with a high, adequately spaced workbench just opposite them. This enables easy turning around from any tool to practically be at the workbench at any time.

Each of the small tools should go in a set of drawers directly under the workbench.

Next to the belt sander, place a low, strong table to pile the belts on and do odd jobs. It could also be useful for riveting and welding. Ensure that it has a piece of railroad track and a manual punch press bolted to it. To place slots in metal pieces for hilts and finger guards, the punch press should be used.

Then you could have a joiner (wood planer) and circular saw at the side out of the way of your regular knife-making area. These tools are used to mill down bigger pieces of wood for making the knife handles.

Having every one of these tools arranged and set up in this way comes in extremely handy for doing numerous other things other than knife making.

Lighting

You will discover that fluorescent lights provide better area illumination and are much more efficient than incandescent bulbs. The incandescent should be used to spotlight the working region of each of the machine. Fluorescent light fixtures are less difficult to locate in second-hand shops that specialize in interior fixtures.

LEAVE A REVIEW?

Throughout the process of writing this book, I have tried to put down as much value and knowledge for the reader as possible. Some things I knew and practice, some others I spent time to research. I hope you found this book to be of benefit to you!

If you liked the book, would you consider **leaving a quick review** for it? It would really help my book, and I would be grateful to you for letting other people know that you like it.

Yours Sincerely,

Wes Sander

CONCLUSION: SELF-EDUCATION

Free lunch doesn't exist. No one is going to teach you everything about a craft just because you ask them to. You may be *extremely* lucky to find somebody who is willing to share their hard-earned knowledge, but they will have expectations that *you* have done your part.

Very few books were available on the craft of blacksmithing in the first half of the twentieth century, but none was available on bladesmithing. About the time the blacksmithing started dying, people in their large numbers started having a renewed interest in it. The outcome is that there are now numerous excellent books on the subject of bladesmithing and knife making, with this book being one of the very best out there.

If you will do any form of bladesmithing, patience and ingenuity are as crucial as inspiration and resolve. Try not to burn yourself out by attempting the actual knife making before you are ready. Prepare yourself as much as you can and take your time about it. Your knives' quality will reflect the way you went about making them. Your evenings should be spent paging through metallurgy and tool-making books.

In the long run, you would realize that bladesmithing is beautiful and the adoration of its maker is contained within its vibratory structure. You would understand that you are putting this affection into the food you eat and the work you do. This consistent subtle reminder of love combined with your everyday food and work can infuse a heightened level of spiritual warmth into a life that might have otherwise been of a mechanical and impersonal nature.

Bonus: Now that you have made a knife that you are proud of, wouldn't it be amazing if you could sell it too?

Get my knife selling secrets with my **100% FREE** e-book, *'Bladesmith's Guide to Selling Knives'*.

Just go to **http://bit.ly/sellknives,** and enter your e-mail.

ADVANCED GUIDE TO BLADESMITHING

FORGE PATTERN WELDED DAMASCUS SWORDS, JAPANESE BLADES, AND MAKE SWORD SCABBARDS

WES SANDER

INTRODUCTION

Do you want to make a knife? It might sound strange to some people, and they might even wonder why they would want to go through such stress when one can easily get inexpensive yet functional knives in stores. I've had the opportunity to be asked a question like this. Some people need a knife that could be in their pocket that they could just use to clean their fingernails and maybe open envelopes; others might be about them getting a hunting knife which they can carry around to spilled-out game if possible so it might not be able owning an expensive knife. Well, a lot more people see a knife as a working tool which should be cared for and, of course, a tool one should have. These people need a knife that is long-lasting; they need a knife that has an edge and can be sharpened easily.

People in the last category can hardly find knives in the stores worthy for them, and the make of the knives they see might not be up to their taste. So, they feel their best bet is making their knives. Making their own is just the best way they can have the kind of quality knife they desired.

For those that want to learn how to make knives and swords, this book is for you. You will be shown how to make them and the stages that are involved and will help save you time from getting inferior knives. Even the advanced stage of the blade markers art such as special parts, fittings and patterns will be discussed.

The good thing is that the materials needed are easily accessible and they are inexpensive. Each knife that you make can be a beauty and a work of art. You will be wowed at the kind of knife you will be able to produce. With this book, they will look smooth and beautiful, having built each with your personal touch. Another good thing about making your blade is that you make the selection of the steel personally so that it will meet what you like so that after heat-treating the blade you can draw the blade, i.e., the temper to meet your specifications. This particular book will give you all the information that you will need to follow.

CHAPTER 1. PATTERN WELDING

Pattern welding can be seen as a unique way of joining a sword blade from iron and steel parts. Many types of iron and steel parts are welded in the fire in such a way that a satisfying pattern can be seen on one or both sides of the knife blade. This pattern comes to be because the two used kinds of iron and steel laid in between the surface shone the light differently, in a particular way after some special polishing and processing. You must use some unique shapes of the parts to be welded to have and create a specific pattern, and again different kinds of iron/steel must be used if one wants to see a visible pattern. This is to say that to succeed with this, structural and compositional piling must be done and should be done in such a way that it produces the kind of pattern one wants. So let look at the different words that relate to ways of making a sword.

Pattern welding: Fire welding makes use of different kinds of iron and steel in a way that a particular kind of pattern occurs on the finished blade. Putting together through fire welding some pieces of iron and steel in a more or less any kind of way will make a pattern on the finished blade. This pattern is often random and isn't intentional. The finished sword is never a pattern welded sword but one done through piling. Patterns will appear if different steels have been used and it will appear at the surface of the sword. It doesn't matter if the steels are automatically different; all that matters is that there are optically different. It is imperative that all the steels on both sides should show at the surface. This is to say that one kind is enclosed by the other kind. Like in producing Japanese blades, you can't possibly see it, and there might be no pattern on it so that the term piling can be used for this.

1. Pattern welded sword is in the class of composite swords.
2. Pattern welded swords are related to the term Damascus, and this often brings a lot of confusion.

Piling

Piling can easily be described as a big piece of iron or steel made by fire welding the smaller pieces. Piling can be done in a casual or complex way. Composite swords and pattern welded swords are readily produced through highly complex piling. Though, a swordsmith can do complex piling in both smart and foolish ways. The foolish way can be welding soft iron for the cutting edges to be hardcore. So, any pattern-welded sword is a sword that was produced by compositional and structural piling; but not all swords produced by compositional and structural piling are said to be a pattern-welded sword just like Japanese swords.

Damascus Technology

This term in history has been used for diverse things, and this has nothing to do with the location of Damascus. The term is said to be introduced because of some mistakes or misunderstanding.

Damascus Swords

Truthfully, no sword emanated from Damascus. Some people do not know this and might believe that a Damascus sword is a better one which has some pattern, though the property of having a very good sword is related to having a good pattern. It should be noted that pattern-welded swords are essential objects of art.

Pattern wielding in its prime was never made because the method was reserved for good swords. One problem with this statement is that nobody has ever seen an old pattern-welded sword so magnificently made. Traditional pattern-welded swords can be said to be 1,000 years old now. The old pattern-welded sword was trended in northern Europe at around 200 AD – 800 AD; but after the last years the slowly made their way out but really these complexities with pattern welding didn't just happen today. There has been a consistent development from piling to complex pattern welding. Earlier, some attempts at structural and compositional did create good swords, and on the side, too, there were simple patterns. Moving beyond this might only beautify the sword, not make the sword better.

How to Make Pattern Welding

Pattern welding uses butt welding. Four rods will be used, and more than ten might be needed. Each piece is 150 mm x 25 mm x 10 mm. Two rods are almost made of same hard steel and readily used for the blade's edges. Then, the rods that will create the pattern are produced from two different plates of steel. A standard that one faces is a package of seven layers, four made from soft steel, while the remaining three are made from hard steel. The hardness doesn't count though. What counts is the bright-dark contrast in the finished blade, not how hard it is. To get this effect, one can use phosphorus-rich and phosphorus-free iron, and this is the common approach in making what is called a striped rod iron, which contains enough phosphorus having a bright whitish appearance, while phosphorous-free iron or steel is dark. So, we will be using neutral terms bright and dark iron or steel. Coupling phosphorus-free carbon-lean and carbon-rich steel isn't a good idea because, during the high-temperature smithing needed for fire welding, the carbon concentration might or might not equalize by diffusion. At this point, there can't be a well-defined color change at the edges any longer. Also, since phosphorus spreads slower than carbon, the difference in phosphorus concentration isn't washed away.

We will be starting with producing a very simple pattern-welded blade with about three patterned striped rods. Some tips you need to know first about simple pattern-welded swords:

1. Get good enough raw material with these specifications
    a. Bright steel—make sure to get phosphorus-rich wrought iron because it is the best.
    b. Dark steel—a phosphorous-free medium will do or whatever will have a variation to the bright steel.
    c. Hard steel—needed for the edge, the steel should have at least eutectoid components about 0.7% carbon; the highest carbon concentration should be considered since one need more carbon during forging.
    d. Other Materials/ Tools needed:
        i. Large File
        ii. Small file set
        iii. Lawnmower blade
        iv. Vise
        v. Angle Grinder discs (cutting, grinding, and finishing)
        vi. Angle Grinder
        vii. Borax

    viii.   Canola Oil

    ix. Tongs

    x. Ferric Chloride

    xi. Anvil

    xii. Forge

    xiii.   Drill (or drill press)

    xiv.   Exotic Wood (Figured Walnut)

    xv. Drill Bits (1/8" and 5/32")

    xvi.   Sandpaper (220-1000 grit)

    xvii. Mini Sledge Hammers

    xviii. Saw (hacksaw)

    xix.   1/8" Brass Pin

    xx. 5/32" Rivet

    xxi.   5-minute Epoxy

    xxii. Palm Sander

    xxiii. Rejuvenating Oil (or wood finish of choice)

    xxiv. Kydex Plastic (or flexible 1/8" plastic)

    xxv.   Torch (optional)

    xxvi. Scrollsaw (optional)

    xxvii. Dremel (optional)

2. Faggot the three materials before you form bars; this means you should drive into a sheet, fold, and weld hammer into a sheet. You can repeat it up to ten times to ensure that the welds are in good condition and avoid putting dirt, influx inclusions, or oxide into the welding. Lastly, make two rods from the hard steel which should be as long as the blade to be, then make 9 – 12 plates from the dark and bright steel

3. Create three packages from three dark and four bright steel plates, i.e., the package, striped rod, and twist.

4. Try and fire weld each package and then drag it out to a rod about the same length as the blade-to-be. The rod's cross-section should be about 1 cm by 1 cm, and at the end, one will have what is called stripe rod. It seems to be the starting material for some pattern-welded swords, though not all.

5. Squeeze the striped rods evenly if you need a more complex pattern. This is to ensure that the alignment of the layers in the non-squeezed regions is the same. You can also change the squeezed direction either clockwise or counterclockwise to have a squeezed striped rod.

6. The next thing to do is to place all rods next to one another. In the non-twisted regions, the layers should be perpendicular to the plane of the picture, so that a stripe pattern can be seen. Try to grind down the rods somehow most especially the flattening sides so it will be easy joining them. You can also try to fit in the squeezed part so that there are fitted like two screws having the same thread. This will mean that the pitch of the squeeze is the same with the two rods, though it might sound impossible. The remaining two hard steel rods will go outside if possible you can bend these rods a bit so that a snug fit is obtained at the end where the point will be.

7. Weld the assembly with fire, ensuring that the weld seams are perfectly done. Forge it into what is the basic sword shape if need be to provide a tang by fire welding it, or better still, stretch the rods into the tang.

8. Create fuller by forging, if necessary. Grind the blade and let it have the cross-section feel. Remember that the pattern you will obtain will be dependent on how deep you grind into the squeezed rods.

9. This is the right time to quench-harden the edges; but before doing this, cover the body with protective mud for the differential hardening stage, making the cooling rate to be higher at the edge part than on the blade's body. By the way, this is a popular way of making Japanese swords with some specific hard edges even the ancestors are believed to have used the same method. At this point temper a bit like annealing at low temperatures after quenching. You can keep the time for the quenching short so that self-tempering can occur since the inside is still very much hot and heat up outside again after you might pull out the blade from the cold quenching liquid. This process can be called slag quenching.

10. Complete it by polishing the blade and forgetting the pattern exposed like etching it and allowing ample time for it to set. Add a good hilt to it, which will help add to the attraction and importance to the blade. By this you have completed a simple welded blade, you might be wondering at this point what a torsion Damascus pattern will look like? I'm longing to meet someone who can visualize what the distribution of dark and bright iron looks like in various depths of a twisted and striped rod. Maybe you can try figuring this out by yourself.

Remember that the front and back will look almost the same; what you see depends on how intense your grinding is and maybe on the chosen cross-sectional shape as schematically indicated. However, how deep you can grind depends a lot on the thickness of the blade. If a thickness of 5 mm is what you want in the center, on each side of a 10 mm rod, you may have to grind off 2.5 mm.

For swords, the ideal size for welding is about 125 x 40mm. Full sheets of 15N20 (1000 x 350mm) and 20C in sheets of 1450 x 260mm will work out to 24 sword pieces of 3mm x 130 x 40mm.

This is to say that you cannot get more flowery or circular patterns farther down the rod. Finally, you have made for yourself a simple yet impressive pattern sword; you might want to try out a more complicated one like having full freedom for patterns, maybe with different patterns on both sides of the blade and a fine pattern, too.

Basic Patterns

The layer count is just the starting point, but you can use less or more of it depending on your preference. In specialized Damascus patterns, such as radials or jellyrolls, fewer layers are needed. It is possible to form weld sections of the high and low-layer bars in a billet via patterning and get a high contrast. Patterning of the flat laminated billet can be achieved in diverse ways. The random pattern needs to be explained though. The layers remain very flat, and some disjointed sometimes occur during forging. Disjointed brings about flat layers to bend, and the result is a smooth organic look to the material. This is outstanding when the edge levels of the blade are finish-ground.

Twist patterns are a bar of the required number of layers that is forged into a square having the corners forged down slightly. The bar gets heated until it's nearing the welding temperature and afterward twisted. This twisting can be slowly done or left tight for diverse effects. The center of each of these twists gives a star effect. Twisted blades are mandated to be left a little thicker than other patterns, as grinding deeper into it makes the star effect more efficient and the whole look more pleasing.

Ladder patterns can be achieved when you grind or press grooves across a Damascus bar. When the pattern is pressed into the blade, it undoubtedly doubles the thickness that was needed in the finished bar. The grooves are then pressed in with dies that are made of round rods and stop blocks that can be used to assist the normal thickness of the finished bar.

When the grooves have been pressed into the bar, it becomes ground flat thereby getting rid of all the high spots. Then, the bar is forged to the needed blade shape, and the pattern of the ladder becomes clear. If the ladder styles are crushed or milled into the bar, they become one-third of the bar thickness. Immediately, the grooves are grounded, the blade then is forged to size forging the whole grooves out of the bar bringing about a different ladder pattern. Now, whether the ladders are pressed or grounded, it should slant from side to side.

Making the raindrop or pool eye pattern is almost the same process as forge welding a ladder pattern, the only difference is the dimples pressed or drilled into the Damascus bar instead of the grooves. The result will be a pattern that resembles a bullseye or raindrops in a pool.

These are the main Damascus patterns and the same patterning techniques, and various others that are used for more complexed patterns. Before moving to more complex patterns and methods, the Damascus steelmaker should become skillful at the forge welding stage.

Complex Pattern Welded Blade

To get this pattern, you need to create eight striped rods, which should have 16 layers each. Then, grind down as deep as you can afford to get your needed pattern on a side and again, you grind down the backside so as to fire weld the thin rods to an extra core; that is four on the front side and another four on the backside. You will need about 64 each of the faggotted dark and bright iron plates for a start, in addition to the hard steel for the edges. What appears will be a sword that is created by piling with a veneer that produces the pattern. Well, the veneer might not all that be important as a sword properties it could just be there as additional material, it helps to hide all the mistakes from large slag inclusions, imperfect welding, and others flaws that might be visible on the made blade.

Making a sword of this magnitude is hard work and need skillful hands because just a mistake like a wrong bang on the hammer or a part of a millimeter not on during grinding can damage the blade. Most ancient sword bearers were mostly about fashion because one enjoys the glamour that comes with sporting a sword even those that can't afford do same. Though some pattern-welded swords had only one side patterned, the last gold hilt spatha that was discovered in 1970 had gold on the show side of the sword only like others. It is on record that this show off pattern-welded sword belonged to an Alemanni that live about 550 AD and near his home town. He was famous for using the plain sax of his sword to harm an opponent. If anyone thinks that the fashion attitude of time past is different from that of today, then he/she needs a rethink, everything has its own time same with a veneered pattern-welded sword. It was loose ground to a more radical new fashion like the ulfberht sword.

How to Create the "W's" Design

"W's" design and mosaic Damascus are other examples of improved designs. While creating the "W's" pattern, the initial billet is piled up like a flat-layered billet; then it is welded. In the lengthening process, the bullet is turned around to form right angles, after which it is hammered to form a rectangular bar with vertical layers. Scales are ground off the bar, cut into sections, and piled up again.

After the second weld arrangement is finished, the layers are still vertical. The bar is recut and piled up again. Scraping the ends of these pieces uncovers the contorted layers are already taking the 'W' form. The third arrangement will further contort the layers and create striking "W's." This pattern is suitable for any number of layers and all the methods of designing like ladders, twists, accordion, and raindrops, as well as help to reveal the design further.

Creating mosaic Damascus is the next stage of intricate design welding. Although the actual components of the mosaic design are still undefined, yet the designs in mosaic Damascus can be seen on the edges of the bar. In 1999, while at the BLADE convention, I asked a few of the most proficient Damascus makers present about their viewpoint on this subject and they all defined mosaic Damascus differently. As the definition is still unclear, every end-grain design will be called mosaic.

Creating Basketweaves, Spider Webs, and Radial "W's"

To some extent, the parquet or basket weave is a simplified mosaic Damascus design and is suitable for a beginner to practice with. To start, hammer a low billet with five to nine layers and lengthen it into square bars one-inch in size. Divide the bar into four sections and pile them up in a square of size two-inch by two-inch with the horizontal layer in the opposite corners and the vertical layer placed in the remaining corners.

Hammer the pile and lengthen the bar out, maintain the square shape of the bar by hammering equally on every side Repeat cutting and welding as explained above creates a fancy basket weave design, a pattern that is suitable as a background filler in a complex mosaic project.

Another example of a basic mosaic pattern is the spider web also known as the spider grid. To produce it, begin with squares if solid steel, like 1050 or 1095. Divide the steel into four squares and pile them up into a square billet, then shims of contrasting steel like 15N20 or pure nickel are added and then welded with a hammer. After this, reshape the billet into a square bar one inch in size. Divide the bar into four sections, pile up and weld again till the preferred grid size is gotten. The grid can be deliberately contorted by hammering it diagonally to give the design a special effect resembling a spider web.

The radial design is another type of mosaic Damascus design A low-layered billet of the flattened sheet is used to start the radial design. A die is used to divide the bar, and this causes an indentation in the center of the layers. Then the halves are divided into four sections, piled up into a square and welded together with a hammer; this creates an effect that makes it look as if the layers radiate outwards from the center of the square.

Exceptional design is created by applying the radical method to a "W's" design. For all the patterning methods, any preferred billet can be used; you might create a remarkable design.

Four-Way and Nine-Way Forging

To achieve the best result in the completed blade, it is necessary to include more than one radial or one jelly roll in the design. A bar can be sectioned into four, piled into a square billet where two sections are arranged in two rows and welded with a hammer; this is called a 'Four-Way.' Also, the bar can be divided into nine sections, and three sections are piled into three rows or a 'Nine-Way.'

To achieve the desired result, the 'Three-Way' or 'Nine-Way' billet can be replicated many times. The size of the blade to be created determines the number of original elements in the completed bar. For large fixed-blade knives, use a minimum of 16 original elements and do the 'Four-Way' two times to achieve that. For small fixed-blade knives, make use of 36 or 64 of the main elements in the bar. A 'Nine-Way' and a 'Three-Way' is needed to accomplish 36 elements whereas doing a 'Four-Way' three times achieves a billet of 64. These values are merely suggestions because the way a bladesmith utilizes the materials is determined by individual preferences.

A single design or several different designs can be mixed in various Four-Way or Nine-Way sequences that accomplishes fascinating designs that have high contrast. The possibilities for producing designs with these combinations are limitless. After combining and welding the preferred amount of elements with a hammer, there are many ways to reveal the design at the end of the bar. Bending the bar and then hammering it into shape will reveal the design along the blade edges. Like in any bent bar, the edge has to be moderately thick to enable more grinding because it is better for the design to be situated close to the center.

To reveal the design, the bar can also be hammered to a rectangular shape by compressing the ladder on the bar or grinding them in. Although I have never applied the raindrop technique, it should expose the pattern on the external part of the rectangular bar as effectively as the ladder method.

The Accordion Technique

This is my most preferred method of revealing an end-grain or mosaic Damascus design. You'll like the illusion of movements and flux that is produced using the Accordion method. Many different techniques can be used to expose a bar like an accordion.

The Damascus bar is hammered into the final length and then hardened. A band saw is used to divide the bar to remove triangles of material from the opposite sides of the bar.

Once all the cutting is completed, a grinder is used to make the sharp edges rounder. This is followed by flattening of the bar. Optimum welding temperature should be used to work on the bar when the accordion is being flattened. If there is a rip in the bar at the bottom, use soldering flux and carefully weld it up. Make the entire bar flat by using one high temperature. Then the bar is hammered to its final length.

The cut-out triangle variant of the Accordion Method will achieve perfect results for you so you'll not need to employ other accordion techniques. The method requires extra hours of labor; but at this point, the

Damascus bar is important, and you'll not be bothered by the effort that would only help you to make the most of the material gotten from the bar.

The Loaf Technique

The Loaf Technique is another method of revealing end-grain designs. It is achieved by welding several blocks alongside each other with a hammer. It is important to enclose the blocks with a protective material, like plain carbon steel or Damascus. The seams are then closed up with a hammer, and the billet welded dry. The weld is made more simple if the blocks fit together perfectly. The Loaf Technique is effectual for designs or figures that require no contortion.

Another way to reveal the design details and create blade material is by cutting tiles from the bar, then using a dovetail to fit them tightly and welding them with a hammer. This technique is complicated, and a beginner is not advised to try this yet. Using a tack, the designs are welded to a protective plate that is ground off after welding with a hammer. This technique also doesn't contort the initial design.

The Plug Method

Now to the final technique used to reveal end-grain designs. The initial bar can be hammered or changed into a rounded bar and plugs are then clipped off. Drill a hole into a blade and insert the plug into the hole. Try to achieve a nice, snug fit while making sure that the plug is a bit thicker than the blade. The blade and plug is assembled and then heated to an optimum temperature and welded in hammer combination or one press. If you like, you can weld a lot of plugs into one blade; this technique also doesn't create contortions.

Sometimes contortions can be used to improve a design or produce an entirely different design. The design in the bar is contorted by hammering a square be in a right-angled bias. The contortion remains as the bar is hammered on the bias until it becomes square back. This can then be used like that or combined into a Four-Way or Nine-Way.

The 'Persian Ribbon'

A design that is ordinary looking can be made more exceptional by contortion. After hammering on a right-angle bias, the squares in a Four-Way are transformed into triangles and can be modified again by another Four-Way to produce diamonds on the design; this method is called the Persian Ribbon. Four blocks are piled up in a square and birders of contrasting materials are wedged between the blocks. They are then welded with a hammer and rotated on a bias, the borders create an 'X' along the bar. The bar is opened with the Accordion Technique. This the 'X' produces the Persian Ribbon design.

Making Custom Images

After the mosaic Damascus pattern has been created, another step is the production of images inside the Damascus steel. It is not uncommon to place images in Damascus; I have seen blades with shamrocks, dragons, mammoth outlines, scenes showing bird-hunting, and many other objects. Utilizing finely ground steel has made it easier to produce these images and figures.

Before the advent of ground steel, an EDM (Electrical Discharge Machine) can be used to carve out an image from two blocks of contrasting steel and the male parts were exchanged. Welding with a hammer produced two bars that had the same figure, one darker than the other. This technique was highly-priced and tough complex detailings could be carved, hammering unevenly still created distortions. If ground steel is used, one block can be carved using the EDM and the figure is then extricated; followed by the pouring of the contrasted ground steel into the empty hole.

Put the male part a square tube and seal the end with a cap, contrasting ground steel is then poured into it and it is welded with a hammer; this produces two bars with the same shoes at half the price of using the EDM.

Another technique for producing images or shapes in steel is to cut plates and pile up the plates. Instead of using the EDM that is more expensive, laser or waterjet can be used to cut the plates. The plates are piled up in a square, and the contrasting ground steel is poured into the already carved out shape; then it is welded with a hammer. It is advisable that the ends of the pile are welded first. This is to compact the plates tightly and prevent powder from passing through the plates. While positioning the shape at the end of the square bar, the billet is then hammered onto the bar; this technique is cheaper than the EDM technique and the materials used are easily accessible.

Casting pure nickel around carved-out molds can also be used to produce shapes. I have carved out wooden shoes of shamrocks, birds, fish, and other objects. This is cheap and requires no tools like the EDM and laser. The nickel form is put in a square tube, and the tube is filled with ground steel. Different shapes can be hammered and put in the billet; you can place any object you want in the billet to achieve the desired result. If ground steel is used, you must compress the powder thoroughly before sealing the tube.

Allowing the tube to vibrate enables the powder to settle and become as compact as possible. While welding with a hammer, initially the bullet feels delicate, but it starts to harden after the bullet is decreased to one-third of its size. Some ground steel moves at a different speed while being forged, so it is important to have a keen knowledge of hammering the bullet with just a little contortion. Start with a basic project and concentrate on how things move in the bullet and the effects can be seen after a little while.

The use of ground steel only started recently; it was introduced in the early 1990s by Steve Schwarzer. There have, however, been a significant advancement in the Damascus steel sector. From my viewpoint, the uses of Damascus steel are endless, and we have barely started maximizing its functions.

Etching the Damascus Steel

There are different ways of engraving in Damascus steel. These are the guidelines on how to etch (or engrave) Damascus steel:

Step 1: Tools and Materials Needed

- Damascus steel
- Engraver-Ferric calories (strength- 42 name)
- Distilled water

- Wire (to suspend the steel in acid)
- Acetone
- Baking soda
- Oil (I used olive oil since the knife would be used for cooking)
- Rubber gloves
- Bucket of water
- Extra fine (000) steel wool
- Plastic or glass containers

Step 2: Steel Cleaning

- Ensure your steel is extremely clean.
- After cleaning, wear the rubber gloves and avoid touching the steel with your bare hands until the entire procedure is finished.
- Immerse in acetone and leave to dry.

Step 3: Acid Bath

- Mix one portion of ferric chloride with three portions of distilled water, and pour in a suitable container. Label the containers, so you won't forget what it is later.
- Hang the piece in the acid. Take it out after ten minutes and immerse it quickly in the bucket of water.

Step 4: Scrub with Steel Wool

- Use steel wool roving to scrub it until you have removed the oxides. The designs should look beautiful.
- Immerse in the bucket of water.
- Is the design intense enough? Otherwise, immerse it in the acetone (see the beautiful picture) and repeat the previous step until the desired result is achieved.
- The knife in the picture was dipped for ten minutes, three times.

Step 5: Repeated Process

- If the intensity of the engraving is to your satisfaction and you have scrubbed for the last time, immerse it in the acetone. Leave it to dry and to get the completed finish, dip it into the acid for three months.
- Avoid touching it at this point. Dip it in the acetone again and then leave it to dry. Acetone dries up quickly so suspending it up would be very unnecessary.

Step 6: Bake and Shake

- Scoop a tablespoon of baking soda into a saucepan of water and heat the piece for ten minutes. This helps to neutralize the acid on the pieces and allows the oxides to set

Step 7: Oil, Not Spoil

- At this stage, use a 2,000 grit sandpaper to sand the steel gently to make it polished and shiny.
- Oil it immediately once you are through; if you don't, it will start to rust.
- If you want, you could apply a clear coat varnish.

CHAPTER 2. A COMPREHENSIVE GUIDELINE TO JAPANESE FORGING

The Japanese technique of swordsmithing requires a great expenditure of effort. It was developed in Japan to create historical Japanese weapons (nihonto) like tanto, nodachi, tachi, odachi, naginata, katana, wakizashi, ya (arrow), uchigatana, nagamaki, and yari. Japanese blades were crafted in various shapes and thickness with different quantities of grind. Wakizashi and tanto are not just scaled-down Katanas; they were crafted with the absence of a ridge (hira-zukuri), or other shapes which were not commonly done on katana.

The art of crafting a Japanese sword blade generally takes days or weeks and was held at 'sacred,' followed by a great exhibition of traditionally religious Shinto rites. Like other couples projects, many craftsmen were involved instead of a single artist. One swordsmith hammered to create a rough shape, and another swordsmith (the apprentice) bent the metal; there was a polishing specialist, an edge specialist. Sometimes, some swordsmiths specialized in the hilt, handguard, or sheath.

Materials and tools

- File
- Vice
- Forge
- Tongs
- Anvil
- Hacksaw
- Bucket of water
- Square hammer, ~3 lbs
- Spray bottle with water
- Cross peen hammer, ~2-3 lbs (optional)
- Safety equipment (apron, gloves, safety goggles, etc)
- 7"×1/8"×5/4" piece of shallow hardening steel

Step 1: Forging

The content of carbon in the steel bloom or kera (manufactured in the tatara) varies; from pig iron to wrought iron. Three kinds of steel are used for the blade—the kind of steel used for the blade core (shingane) had low carbon content and was called hocho-tetsu. The outer skin of the blade (kawagane) was formed from a combination of steel with high carbon content, tamahgene, and the remelted pig iron (nabe-gane or cast iron).

Procedure:

The folding of the steel is the most understood stage in the production process. Here, the sword blades are created by repeated heating, hammering, and folding of the metal. Folding makes the metal stronger and free of impurities, this was an innovation of legendary Japanese swordsmiths.

1. Japanese swords are crafted by folding the low-carbon iron on itself many times to remove impurities; this yields the soft metal that is used for the blade core.
2. The high-carbon steel and the cast iron (with a higher carbon content) are then hammered in rotating layers.
3. The cast iron is heated, dipped in water, and divided into small sections to remove slag.
4. The steel is then hammered into a single plate while the sectioned cast iron are stacked on top and the entirety is welded with a hammer into a single billet; this is known as the age-kitae technique.
5. The billet is then lengthened, divided, folded, and welded with a hammer again.

The ways of folding the steel can be: longitudinal (sideways) or transverse (from the front backward). Both folding directions can be employed to achieve the preferred grain design; the procedure is called shita-kitae and can be repeated eight times or even up to 16 times. After folding 20 times (2^{20} or 1,048,576 separate layers), the carbon content would have spread evenly, creating homogenized steel; thus, folding no longer produces an effect. The quantity of carbon used determines the type of steel produced, maybe the hard steel used for the edge (hagane), or the moderately hard spring steel (kawagane) used for the back and sides.

In the last few folding, the steel may be hammered into many thin plates, piled up, and welded with a hammer to form a brick. The steel grain is delicately placed between close layers. Note that the portion of the steel used to produce the blade determines the actual arrangement

With each folding and heating, a mixture of water, clay, and straw ash are used to coat the steel to limit it from oxidizing and carburizing. The clay is to give room for a favorable environment. The formation of a wustite layer is boosted by the clay and water at about 1.650F, which is equivalent to 900C. This kind of formation occurs when oxygen is absent. The silicon which is already present in the clay will then come in contact with the wustite to form fayalite, and the fayalite will turn liquid at about 2,190F. The liquid we have now will stands as a flux, bringing and drawing out impurities when it's squeezed from the layers. With this, a pure surface is obtained which will then help the forge-welding process to be accomplished. With the loss of impurities, slag, and even iron as sparks during the hammering process, the weight of the steel will be reduced and becomes even lighter. This process is so popular now because it uses the impure metals which come from the low temperature that is needed in the smelting of it at this particular time and place.

Folding helps to achieve the following:

- It gives an alternative layer of different hardenability. This is to say that during quenching, the high-carbon layers becomes harder than when the medium carbon is used. These two the hardness of high carbon and low-carbon steels combine to form property of toughness.
- It removes any emptiness in the metal.
- It helps to hold the metal within the layers and making an even spread of other elements like the carbon throughout the individual layers which help increase the effective strength and thereby reduce the number of initial weak points.
- Folding helps to eliminate plenty of impurities which help fight the poor quality of raw Japanese steel.
- It helps to provide about 65,000 layers through daily decarburizing its surface and also bringing this too to the blades interior and also assisting in giving the swords their needed grain.

Step 2: Assembly

The high-quality Japanese sword is made from different distinct types of steel. The manufacturing process employs the use of various steel types at different parts of the sword. Maru (or muku) is the main type of modern wakizashi and katana, which is the most used, and the whole sword is made up of single steel. The good thing now is that the modern steels are being used which made the sword to be strong and no longer fragile like what has been registered from history. Another type—the kobuse type—is composed of two sheets of steel, which are called hagane, otherwise known as edge steel, and shingane, also known as core steel. The last types are called Honsanmai, shihozume, and kawagane.

There are numerous ways these steel can be assembled, which differs from one goldsmith to another.

1. The edge-steel is dragged out, bent into a U-shape and the softcore steel is then pushed into the hard piece of it.
2. This is then welded together and nailed into the basic shape of a sword.
3. At the end of this, the two plates of steel are put together.

The difference between the two is just in their hardenability. When it comes to more complex construction, it can mainly be used with antique weapons. Various modern weapons are constructed this way with either one, two, or three sections.

Another process that can be used is

1. Put together the pieces into a block and forge weld it together.
2. Drag out the steel and make into a sword so that the steels will end up being in its correct place as it ought to be.

This method is mostly used for more sophisticated models, which enable effective parrying devoid of fear of destroying the side of the blade. Now to make honsanmai or the shihozume types, it all about gathering the pieces of hard steel and putting it to the outside of the blade in the same way. It just that these types shihozume and soshu are not easily accessed, but they give very rear support.

Step 3: Heat Treatment for Japanese Blade

This is the point the Japanese process of sword making will be appreciated. When forging has been done, the steel will still retain its hardness. Without further treatment, this hardened blade will be brittle. Therefore, it is subjected to heating till it attains the right softness level.

Heat treatment is the tempering and quenching of the steel. Tempering is done by heating the blade to about 400^0F, while quenching is done by rapid cooling.

Heat treating makes steels flex and strength to react in various ways. When steel cools quickly, it will be martensite, that is being very hard and brittle, but slower makes it pearlite which makes it bends easily and it doesn't hold an edge. But if one needs the combination of the two, a different hard-treatment should be used. In differential hardening or what is known as differential, quenching is a process whereby the sword is painting with layers of clay before heating and a thin layer is provided at the edge of the sword which boosts fast cooling to bring fast hardness for the edge. Afterward, a thicker layer of clay will be applied to it, too; this will bring about slower cooling. This will bring about softer, resilient steel, giving the blade the ability to absorb shock without breaking. Another name for this process is called the differential tempering, though this is a different type of heat treatment.

If one needs to bring out a difference in hardness, then the steel should be cooled at a different duration and again by controlling the thickness of the insulating layer. Even the Japanese by being able to control the different rates of the heating and cooling speeds of the sword blades, they were able to manufacture blades that had a softer body and a hard edge.

This Japanese process has brought about two major effects on the swords:

- Making the blade always to curve.
- Bringing a clear boundary between soft and hard steel.

When the heat is quenched, the less-heated edge will contract, which will make the sword to bend firstly toward the edge; but unfortunately, the edge can't contract fully before reaching the martensite forms, since the remaining part of the swords is still very hot and also in a thermally expanded state due to the heat. However, the sword spine will still be hot and pliable for several seconds, but will later contract even more than the edge which makes the sword to still bend away from the edge, of course, this helps the swordsmith have an easily curving blade. Again, this will make the differentiated hardness and the methods of smoothing the steel result in what is called Hamon, which means hardening pattern or tempering line. The Hamon can be described as the noticeable outline of the yakiba, which is used as a means to assess both the beauty and quality of the finished blade. Hamon patterns come from the various manners in which the clay is used. There can act as some style for sword molding or better still a mark that a swordsmith is known for. The difference in how hard steel can be done better when put near the hamon. This will help to show different layers or parts of the blade which includes the intersection between an edge from the edge-steel and the sides which are produced from the skin-steel.

To get the right thickness of the edge's coating then there should be a right balance of temperature of water. Also, the right hardness of the edge can be achieved without one needing any tempering. In some cases though, the edge will turn out very hard, so the best bet will be equitably tempering the whole blade for a while so that the hardness will be to a minimal level which will be suitable for the edge. The suitable hardness normally is between HRc58-60. Heat treatment helps reduce the martensite hardness and make it become tempered martensite. Pearlite doesn't work well with tempering and doesn't even change in hardness

Step 4: Finishing (Polishing, Mounting, and Sheathing)

When the swordsmith fully does the rough blade, the smith will then put the blade in a polisher, which is known as togishi. The work of togishi is to sharpen the shape of the blade and add artistic value to the blade. This whole process takes ample time and might run into weeks. Olden days polishers were using like three types of stone, but these present polishers are using seven types. The modern high level of polish came to be around 1600 because then the emphasis was placed more on functionality than its form. Polishing processes always took more time than crafting, which helps to heighten the beauty of a blade is usually good polish while bad polisher damage even the best of blades. A novice in the polishing business will create a bad blade which can forever damage it.

Saya in Japan is known as a scabbard for a katana. The handguard piece is created as one's work of art, and in the Edo period, it was known as tsuba. Mountings are done when the blade is finished, and the job is passed to the mountings-maker also known as a maker. Sword mountings take different shapes in a different era but wholly, it all about the same idea, the difference only lies in the elements used and then the form of wrapping. The visible part of the hilt includes a metal or a wooden grip, which is known as the tsuka and can be said to be the entire hilt. The handguard or tsuba which is on the Japanese swords which are very small and round is produced of metal and often stylish. It has a wrapping called menuki, and there always a decoration beneath it, and it has a pommel at the base which is called a kashira. A bamboo peg known as mekugi is fastened around the tsuka and also through the tang of the blade, the drilling of it is done with a peg hole. This helps to set the blade securely into the hilt. To fasten the blade tightly into its sheath, the blade has a collar or what is known as habaki which stretches an inch past the handguard, and this will help keep the blade from damages.

Producing sheaths aren't easy; we have two types of sheaths, and the two require great work to produce. One type is the shirasaya, which is largely created from wood and is known as the resting sheath, which is used as the storing sheath. The other type is the decorative and battle-ready sheath, which is also known as a jindachi-zukuri, that's used from the obi, by straps or buke zukuri if it thrust through the obi. Kyu-gunto, shin-gunto, kai-gunto are all types of mounting that were used in the 12th-century military.

CHAPTER 3. STAINLESS STEEL FORGING OF FULL TANG KNIFE

This is about how a full tang knife is made from stainless, though it is good to do self-research because the climatic conditions also affect the stainless steel. Creating one's tools has always been an awesome thing, knives inclusive. From the stone age until now, knives have always been a valuable part of a man either as outdoor protection or what should be used in the home as a basic tool and, of course, it is what should be produced to your taste and style. Well, we have numerous ways on how we can produce a knife. There are tried and tested methods, but this underneath method can work excellently for stainless steel forging.

Materials/ Tools needed:

- Files
- Drill
- Dremel
- Epoxy
- Forge
- Anvil
- Forge
- Clamps
- Grinder
- Hammer
- Tongs (or big pliers)
- Hot cutter
- Quench tub
- Linseed oil
- Angle grinder or hacksaw
- Steel (5/32" X 1 1/4" X 96")
- Handle Material (see handle section)
- Sandpapers of varying grits from about 120-1000.

Step 1. Designing the knife on paper—Materials needed

Graph paper, Metal Ruler, French curve, Normal pencil

Generally, the best bet in making anything is first to design it and doing the same with a knife isn't a bad idea. Having the material display of one will enable you to see all that you need to work with.

Step 2: Basic design on paper—The blade and the handle

The main focus when it comes to knife production should be the blade, and the handle and your focus should be on this two; nonetheless, time can still be put in other parts like the pommels and the guards. If you have a band saw then other parts would be easy to make. Freehand rendering can be used for the designing of the knife. If you like the basic proportion, then you can go ahead. It is always good for you to design what you like and what looks delightful to your eyes.

Step 3: Basic design on paper—Designing the blade

The first thing a person notices about a knife is its blade and as such more attention should be paid when designing it. The blade should give the knife a better outlook and uniqueness. You can make do with a simple blade with nothing complex about it. Starting with something simple will bring about less grinding, and it will perform better. So you should start with cutting about an 8-inch by 1.75-inch blade, then drew out a curve, design it to taste and get it ready to be taped to its stock.

Step 4: Making the blade proper—Melting and casting

First, melt the raw materials together. This will be done in an electric furnace. Usually, this step requires intense heat of about 8 – 12 hours. After melting, cast the molten steel into semi-finished forms, including slabs, tube rounds, rods, blooms of rectangular shapes, and billets of round or square shapes (about 1.5 inches thick).

Step 5: Making the blade proper—Forming

After melting and casting, the semi-finished steel undergoes its forming and shaping operations. This starts with hot rolling, whereby the semi-finished is heated and passed through huge rolls. The billets are formed into a short bar of ¼ inch or ⅛-inch thick (for a full-tang knife).

Step 6: Making the blade proper—Heat treatment

Heat treatment (also called annealing or tempering) is done after the steel has been formed and shaped. This is the heating and cooling of the steel under specific conditions to make the metal soft. Whether it's austenitic, ferritic, or martensitic, different steels have different temperature requirements. Austenitic steels are heated at temperatures above 1900^0F, depending on its thickness. It is sometimes important to clean contaminants from the surface before heat treating.

Some steels also go through age hardening, a heat treatment for higher strength which is done with great care. The properties of the steel can be affected by changes in recommended temperature, cooling rate, or time. Higher strength is produced from lower aging temperatures while a lower strength and tougher material is formed from high-temperature aging. The heating rate to attain the required aging temperature is 900 to 10000F.

Quenching is the rapid cooling done after heat treatment. It increases the steel's toughness while retaining its strength. One recommended process of quenching is by using water, whereby the material is dipped in a 35^0F ice-water bath for at least two hours. Thick sections are quenched using water while thin sections are quenched using air cooling or blasting. Cooling must not be done slowly so as to avoid carbide precipitation. Thermal stabilization can be done to eliminate buildup by holding the steel at $1500 - 1600^0$F.

Step 7: Making the blade proper—Descaling

After tempering, scales or build-up are sometimes formed on the steel. These can be removed in several ways—one of which includes pickling. Pickling is done by bathing the steel in nitric-hydrofluoric acid to descale it. Another method of removing the scales is electrocleaning. In electrocleaning, a cathode and phosphoric acid are used to apply electric current to the steel's surface to remove the scale. Depending on the steel type being used, tempering and descaling of the steel are done at different stages.

The knife steel bar goes through added forming steps including more hot rolling, forging, or extruding after the first hot rolling before annealing and descaling are done.

Cold rolling is the passing of the steel through rolls low temperature. Cold rolling leads to reduced thickness and makes the steel ready for final processing.

Step 8: Making and grinding the shape of the blade

This is one step that doesn't need you exerting much energy considering it a simple step; the only tool needed here is the bench grinder. Though you can still use an angle grinder, the con is that you can hardly see what you are doing and even getting straight edges might be difficult. Ensure you have your safety gear on and wear clothes that you might not be bothered with any longer after the grinding since you would be covered in metal. In this step, the knife will be taking shape already.

Step 9: Making the blade and grinding the Bevel

You have to be careful with this step because the cutting edge is like the most important process, so when trying to set it, you need to go gently and slow with it. So on each side, try to grind away half of the edge and be sure that you tightly clamp the blank. Maybe a C clamp can be used since the cover less of the knife considering it wouldn't allow it to move anywhere while grinding. To form the bevel use a 36 grit wheel for the angle grinder because it will help create a wide cutting path. When forming always look down the blank to check the angle, when you're halfway gone, flip it over to the other side and grind. Watch out when once you see a wire edge forming then you can stop, because you have succeeded in making a perfect edge.

Step 10: Making the blade—Rust removal and finishing

This is the part where the almost finished knife is taking shape. Finishing is all about making the knife shine; it is another important process in producing a knife. To achieve this use an angle grinder with a grit flap wheel of 120. Remember to clamp it tightly to the Adirondack chair, concentrate your effort on the blade, and maybe on the handle area too, so clean them to remove all the rust to look very clean, then hand sand it by clamping the knife tightly to a block of wood then clamp that in a vise. Start with 180 grit and work it up to about 1,000 grit. This will help give the knife a nice smooth satin finishing. If you still desire, use rough sandpaper on the handle to help the epoxy stick more. Stop when you have a nice shiny blade and move to the next step.

Step 11: Making the handle—Rough cutting and gluing

To begin this step, you need to start with creating the handle scales. Scales are those pieces that we see on either side of a blade. To make the scales, the size should be measured out by putting the knife on the wood and marking out the largest dimensions that are needed. With a square, mark out a rough rectangle, and cut it off, this can be done with the aid of a table saw since it's faster and easy to use, but hand saw is still good though it needs a lot of patience. Cut out the scales and then glue them together, mix up a good bit of glue and spread it on the scale and then place the knife on the scale, repeat it also on the other scale. Get them lined up and clamp them, you can wait for some hours like two hours before using the knife; this will give the knife plenty of time to set.

Step 12: Creating the Handle—Getting the Right Thickness

My findings have shown that knife handles should not be thicker than ¾-inch, but if the knife is bigger than the usual, you'd have to increase the thickness a bit. Adjust your calipers to half of your desired thickness and begin to scrape with a rasp. A plane can be used if you like. Keep filing till you achieve the right thickness on both ends. If the rasp you are using is sharp, this shouldn't take time; ensure to file equally on both edges.

Step 13: Creating the Handle—Rough Shaping

This is the most tiresome and lengthiest step. Here, the handle closely resembles a handle and not a block of wood. You need to be insightful for this step because you are required to know the point where the metal starts. Striking a wood rasp on metal makes it duller. The simple logic is to continue using the rasp until you can feel that you are getting close to metal, and then change to a file that can be used for both wood and metal. This part is moderately tiresome, but you can't afford to rush when doing this. You can now see the primary design taking form which is what is required at this stage. Also, you might want to wrap the blade using duct tape so it can be clamped in the vise and you can keep working on the entire handle.

Step 14: Creating the Handle—Final Sanding and Fixing Pins

You are almost through, all that is left is sanding and pins. As the name implies, sanding is working through the grits till it is about 320 or 400; you can play around and increase or up to 1,000, but I am not sure it would change the texture of the knife. The knife handle here was sanded up to 320 grits before final touches were added.

I would be explaining how to fix the pin and adding final touches since they are done at the same time. Drill a hole through the handle and blade, glue the pins in with epoxy and then file them flat.

Marking the holes is the initial step in this process. Make a rough estimate of the marks first, then check if they are aligned using a straightedge. The next step is to measure your pins and cut them. To measure, place them on the handle and use a sharpie to mark. Create room for error; make it a bit bigger. Removing material is easier than adding to it. Using a vise, clamp the rod and use a simple hacksaw to cut the pins off.

Next is the drill press. Clamp the piece firmly and drill through everything at the same time. It's best to set the drill to the lowest speed and use a very sharp bit. Do this again with as many pins as you desire. When you are through, recheck how well the pins fit in the holes. You are very fortunate if they barely fit; tap them in using a mallet and file the ends off. If they are loose instead, then it's time for epoxy glue! Make another epoxy mixture and rub a little at the middle of the pin, slide it in and clean off left-over epoxy with a dry cloth. Before filing, allow to dry. When you are sure it is dry, use a mill file to file the pins.

Step 15: Make the Handle—Complete it all!

This is the final production step! This step is not compulsory. You can decide to have your handle left as bare wood if you like. You could also treat it with a little Danish oil and two coats of polyurethane. The method for applying oil is easy. Clean off the handle with a clean cloth, then using a rag, apply oil; ensure to cover the entire handle. Used two coats and left them throughout the night. Before adding the polyurethane, with the finest grit earlier used, mildly sand the surface using 320 grit. Then make sure to clean off all the sawdust again with a clean cloth. Apply a very light coat of polyurethane to the wood using a film brush. Use two coats and sand before each coat. After the last coat, leave it for 24 hours. This allows it to set fully. Congrats! The manufacturing process is complete.

Step 16: It is time to sharpen!

Your knife finally becomes a tool at this stage. It is important to get a razor-sharp edge on a knife, but this can be a bit hard with a handcrafted knife. Using your hand to grind the edges unavoidably results in irregularities, but this is expected as part of handcrafting your tool. Little errors like this can be fixed, so do not despair. To sharpen the knife, it's best to use a sequence of stones: a coarse, followed by medium, and then fine stone. Work through your stones till you achieve a very sharp edge. After this, you can choose to leave it that way or sharpen the edges on a strop. This gives your knife a razor-sharp edge. To try out the edges, slice up some paper, it should cut through perfectly. If it doesn't, continue. When you can constantly slice up paper into ribbons using your knife—you are through!

Step 17: Congratulations!

At the end of this, your full tang stainless steel knife is completed. There is a feeling of contentment when you use a tool you made by yourself and see it work equally as good as, or better than knives bought in the store. Additionally, it is a good skill to be able to create a tool from scratch (in case the zombies arrive!).

Be careful and enjoy your new knife.

CHAPTER 4. EXOTIC HANDLE MAKING, WOOD, AND METAL FINISHING

Knife handles and handcrafted swords have a distinct attractiveness to them.

Sword handles are fashioned to support and improve the beauty and safety of a specific sword type. The sort of handle you would create must properly for your selected sword. The procedure for creating custom-made knife handles may take a lot of time, but it is simple as long as you know the steps.

Luckily, you would eventually have a beautifully customized knife to display proudly. This segment will help you learn how to make the most common European sword—a hidden tang, screw-on pommel sword handle. Because handcrafted items do not have generalized specifications, measurements are determined by the blade you are designing the handle for.

Materials/ Tools needed:

- Files
- Scribe
- Clamps
- Epoxy
- Drill Press
- Knife Blade
- Metal Sanders
- Metal Band Saw
- Wood Band Saw
- Masking Tape
- Sand Papers (200-600)
- Handle material (could be wood or plastic or stone etc)
- Pins - Mosaic, Solid, or Rivets (optional)
- Color spacers to add lines of color between metal knife handle and your wood (optional)

Steps to Creating Knife Handles
Part 1. Getting the Base and Materials Ready

1. Create or get a full tang knife blade—the constituents of a full-tang knife blade are a bare metal handle and a metal blade. The part of the handle (tang) should already be cut in the same shape as the wooden handle (scale). You can shop online for knife kits that have only the full-tang blade and pins.
2. Cover the blade end of your knife with three layers of tape.

Duct tape or electrical tape would be perfect. Masking tape can be used, but more layers would have to be added. Cover the tips of the knife through to the base—the point where the blade ends—with the tape. Do not wrap the tang. Ensure that the blade is entirely covered with the tape; this will prevent the knife from cutting you, or epoxy glue from dropping on the blade.

In addition to preventing you from getting cut, the tape also protects the blade from breaking off or scratching.

If you can still touch the blade through the tape, cover the blade with more layers of tape.

1. Select two 1/4-in (0.64 cm) pieces of wood for the scales. Select a strong, long-lasting wood about 1/4-in (0.64cm) in thickness and a bit bigger than the tang. For a better finish, make sure the grain is of the same length as the wood. These pieces can be bought online from stores that deal in knife-making materials.

A knife handle is made of two halves which are also called 'scales.' The tang is placed in between the scales.

Excellent examples of wood to use are pear, apple, ash, hickory, bois d'arc, and pecan. Hardwoods are gotten from deciduous trees and generally last longer than softwoods gotten from coniferous trees.

2. If required, cut the ponds. If you bought a knife kit, the pins might have been cut already. If you didn't buy a kit, you are required to cut the metal rod onto one-inch (2.5 cm) lengths. Place the rod on a stable surface and use a file or a metal bar to cut it into one-inch (2.5 cm) lengths.

The number of holes in the tang determines how many rods can be cut. While a few knives have two holes, others have four. The metal rods have to be thin enough to fit the holes in the tang correctly. For every knife, the thickness of the rod differs.

3. If required, file down the pin ends. Again, if you bought the knife kit, the pins would be already filed; but if you cut the pins by yourself, the ends will probably be bristled, smoothen it using a metal file or a grinder.

Do not be distressed of the ends of the pins are not completely flat. You would still file them down later to make them aligned with the scales.

4. Using a plastic wrap and plywood, line your clamps and vice. Though you would not need this until it is time to glue everything, it takes a short time for epoxy glue to set, so, it would be easier to have prepared everything. Connect plywood to each end of your vice. Get a sheet of plastic wrap, fold it like a taco and tuck it between the vices. If you have one, use heavy-duty vice mounted on a table. If you don't, instead, use two or three vices.

The plywood prevents the vices from making an indent on the wooden scales. The plastic wrap prevents the epoxy glue from dripping around. Wax paper can be used in place of a plastic wrap.

Part 2: Drilling the Pin Holes

1. Wrap duct tape around both the scale and tang. Pile the scales on top of each other with your desired sides placed outside, with the handle facing out. Place the tang on top and wrap a piece of masking tape around the center to grip everything firmly.

Ensure to leave the holes in the tang open.

If the wrapping tape is not firm enough, wrap another layer of tape around the end of the scales and tang. Masking tape is perfect to be used here because it has a powerful hold and also leaves just a little residue.

2. With the tang's hole as a guide, use a drill press to make the first hole. With the tang facing upward, place the knife down on the drill plate. Put in the drill bit into one of the tang holes. Power up the drill and press down on it. Ensure to go through both scales. Power off the drill press and bring lift out the bit. With a drill press, this is much easier to do; a handheld drill can do the same thing, too.

3. Insert a pin in the tang hole and do the rest. If there are four holes in your tang instead of two, the position of the second hole oblique is oblique to the first. Insert the pins and drill the remaining two holes obliquely across each other. Insert the pins immediately you are done drilling the holes. Drilling the holes and inserting the pins one after the other will prevent the tank and the scale from slipping.

Tap the pins in using a hammer.

4. Take off the tape and trace the tang onto the scales. Remove the piece of the tape, but do not touch the pins and tang. Using a marker, trace the outline of the tang. The type of marker used- whether temporary or permanent is not important, as you will still sand this off later.

5. Take away the tang and cut off the scales. Set the tang and do not take the pins out of the scales. Outside the outline you have traced, cut the scales with a band saw, or a scroll saw. Later, you would sand the scales to suit the tang.

You have to cut through both scales concurrently. The scales will be held firmly together by the pins.

6. Sand and shine the top edge of the scales. After you put the knife handle together, it would be impossible to sand and shine the narrow edge on top that is touching the blade at the base.

The blade might cause an obstruction, so you had better do this now. Just tape the scales together, sand and polish the top edge to your satisfaction. Shape the edge with a belt sander. Use a 220 and 400-grit sandpaper to sand down the edges. Complete with a buffer. It would even be better to get the pins inserted into the scales. This would make sure that the scales are well-positioned and equal.

Part 3: Gluing the scales

1. Clean both edges of the tang to get rid of oils and dirt. You could use rubbing alcohol or a window cleaner. Just rub your preferred solution down the tang and allow to dry. After this, do not touch the tang with your hands alone.

Rubbing alcohol gives a better result, but window cleaner can be used as well. It is not necessary to clean the wood scales. The texture and porosity of the wood enable it to absorb the epoxy completely.

2. Scrape the tang on both ends to allow the epoxy to adhere firmly. A metal file or a screw can be used for this. No precision is needed for this step, but you have to clean the surface properly as soon as you are through. If there are no bumps or irregularities on the marked side of the scale, it would be good if you scrape them too. The scales can also be sanded roughly with 120-grit sandpaper.

Ensure to scrape only the sides that would be in contact with the tang.

3. Follow the instructions and mix the epoxy glue. There are different brands of epoxy glue, but mostly, you will be required to prepare the same amounts of 'Quantity A' and 'Quantity B' in a disposable plastic cup. Do this quickly because it takes a short time for most epoxy glue to set. Confirm that you are using epoxy glue and not epoxy coating or resin.

Stir the mixture using a disposable tool, because the glue damages whatever you mix it with. Wearing some plastic or vinyl gloves are recommended. Epoxy glue can be purchased in hardware stores; some craft stores also sell them.

4. Using the already prepared epoxy, glue the first scale to the tang. Evenly spread a layer of the mixed epoxy, using a disposable knife or a paint spatula on one of the sides of the tang and the side marked on the matching scale. Press both the scale and the tang together.
5. Get the pins inserted and the second scale glued. Working very fast, turn the knife over so you will be able to see the tang from the other side. Get the pins inserted into the holes. Coat the tang and the marked side of the scale left, and then press them together.

You might need to hammer the other scale to make sure it fits firmly. You can use epoxy to coat the pins if you like. This will further strengthen the bond.

6. Place the handle into the vise and firmly clamp it. Ensure that the handle is inserted between the pieces of plastic wrap- in this manner, the epoxy glue would not spill around. Clamp the vise as firmly as possible.
7. Clean excess epoxy with an acetone-soaked rag. After pressing the two handles together tightly, excess epoxy drips down. With a rag dipped in epoxy, clean excess epoxy that might have dripped down from between the scales.
8. Leave the epoxy to set. The type of epoxy used determines how long this would take. Some are set and available for use under one hour; others could take up to a whole day to dry. Confirm the hours it takes to dry and instructions on the label.

Part 4. Completing the Handle

1. Remove the knife from the vice. As soon as the epoxy has set, loosen the vise and remove the knife. Still, leave the tape around the blade.

2. If required, grind away excess pins. Use a belt sander or grinder to grind off excess pins protruding out of the surface of the scale. They have to be aligned with the scale. Sculpt and shape the belt handle with a belt sander.

3. Continue sanding the scales up till the metal part of the tang. Sand off any lines left from tracing the outline of the tang onto the scale. Now, you can sand off the edges of the handle to make them more rounded and easier to handle.

4. Sand and polish the scales. Start sanding the scales using 220-grit sandpaper. When the wood is smooth, switch to 400-grit sandpaper. Complete with a buffer until the sales are polished to your utmost satisfaction.

5. If you like, seal the handle. For a better finish, you can add two coats of oil-based polyurethane and one coat of dewaxed shellac. After it dries, polish it until it shines. The type of brand used determines the amount of time it takes to dry. So, make sure to read the label properly. The time taken could range from a few hours to some days.

6. Take off the tape from the blade. Your knife is now finished and ready for use. You can scrape off any epoxy remaining on the blade using a craft blade, but ensure to do this along the length of the blade. Acetone can also be used to dissolve the excess glue.

CHAPTER 5. EXOTIC HILTS MAKING

The handle of the sword is called the hilt (sometimes referred to as haft). The hilt consists of a guard, pommel, and grip. The guard might contain a quillon or cross-guard; sometimes, though rarely, a ricasso might also be present. A sword knot or tassel might be connected to either the pommel or the guard.

Pommel

The origin of the word pommel is Anglo-Norman, and it means little apple. The pommel is an enlarged fixture at the top of the handle. Initially, they were created to stop the sword from sliding off the hand. In Europe, during the 11th century, they were designed to be weighted enough to provide a form of stability for the blade. This allowed the sword to be balanced close to the hilt, giving room for variability of fighting techniques. The opponents may also be struck using some (as in the Mordhau technique); this depends on the specific sword design and swordsmanship technique. Pommels have been shaped in different forms. Various designs can be etched onto them and are sometimes decorated and adorned with jewels. In the 1964 book, *The Sword in the Age of Chivalry,* written by Ewart Oakeshott, he established a classification system for medieval pommels, in addition to his previous blade typology. Ewart Oakeshott pommel types are represented with alphabets A to Z, while the variants are represented with numerals.

A - A derivative of the typical Viking sword, the classical "Brazil-nut" pommel.

B - A shorter and rounded form. B1 is the subtype with a straight lower edge- "mushroom or tea rosy."

C - The derivative of the Viking sword in the shape of a "cocked-hat."

D - A larger sized and later modification of C.

E - A modification of D with an angular top.

F - A modification of D with a much more angular top.

G - A plain disk. G1- disk pommel designed with flower-shaped ornaments. G2- disk-shaped variant with a shell-like ornament. Both are specifically made in Italy.

H - A disk with beveled edges. One of the most widely used types, seen in the 10th to 15th century. H1- an oval variant of H.

I - A disk with wide beveled edges; though the internal disk is smaller in size than H.

J - Similar to me, but here a deep groove is made in the beveled edges. J1- a modified variant of the classic wheel-pommel.

K - A modified variant of J with extensively wide and flat edges, common in the Middle Ages.

L - "trefoil-shaped," tall, rare, seen exclusively in Spain in the 12th and 13th centuries.

M - A subsequent modification of the multi-lobed Viking pommel type, seen commonly on tomb figurines in Southern Scotland and Northern England around 1250 – 1350, rarely seen now as only a few are remaining. Check Cawood sword.

N - In the form of a boat, not commonly seen in art or even surviving specimens.

O - An uncommon variant formed like a crescent.

P - An uncommon variant shaped like a shield. The only known example is seen at Nuremberg cathedral, on a statue.

Q - Pommels shaped like a flower; only seen from artistic sword drawings.

R - Uncommon pommel in the shape of a sphere. Only existed in the 9th and 10th centuries.

S - An uncommon cube-shaped type with the edges removed.

T - Shaped like a fragrance stopper (looks like the stopper on the top of a fragrance), also looks like a fig or pear. First seen in the early 14th century, but became common after 1360 with subsequent modifications till the 16th century. T1 and T2 are the main subtypes.

U - Seen only in the late 15th century, shaped like a key.

V - Common in the 15th century, shaped like a 'fish-tail.'

W - In the form of a 'misshapen wheel.'

Z - In the form of a square. Variants can be used to pinpoint the area and era found. Z1 and Z2b variants were common in South Eastern Europe. Z3 was typically Venetian swords shaped like a 'cat-head.' Z4- common in Serbia and Bosnia.

Grip

The handle of the sword is the grip made from metal or in some cases, wood, normally covered with shagreen (tough, untanned leather or the skin of a shark). Sharkskin lasted longer in temperate climates but lost form in hot climates. Rubber later became widely used in the late 19th century. Although other sword types might use the skin of a ray fish, referred to as "same" in katana construction. Regardless of the material used to cover the grip, it was glued on and supported with a wire helically coiled around.

Guard

It has been commonly misinterpreted that protection is provided by the crossguard for the user's whole hand against the opponent's swinging. The full handguard was only used when the shield and armored gauntlet were abandoned. There are no actual guards on the early swords; they only had a stopper-kind of material to stop the hand from moving on to the blade when thrusting.

Beginning from the 11th century in Europe, the guards began to take on different shapes. They were shaped like a straight crossbar (later referred to as quillon) at right angles to the blade. And from the 16th century, they were made more sophisticated with branches, curved bars, and loops to give the hand protection. One curved piece side-by-side with the fingers (approximately parallel to the blade or the handle and at right angles to the cross-guard) was called 'knuckle-bow.' Subsequently, the bars could be complemented or substituted with metal plates that were pierced decoratively.

The word 'basket-hilt' was then coined to describe these designs, and there were different types of these basket-hilt swords. At the same time, the insistence of thrust attacks with small swords and rapiers exposed the level of unprotectedness of thrusting.

By the 17th century, there was a production of guards that introduced a solid shield that covered the blade externally up to the diameter of about two inches or greater. Preceding variants of these guards retained a single quillon or quillons. But quillons were absent in subsequent variants, thus, they were all together referred to as 'cup-hilt.' The guards of modern foils and epees were created using this subsequent variant as the prototype.

Ricasso

This is the dull section of the blade directly beneath the guard. It is protected by an extension of the guard. The ricasso allows the position of a third-hand on two-handed swords enabling the user's hands to be spread wider for a higher advantage.

Hilt Assemblage

To maximize the sword functions, it is important that the hilt is made the right way. The weight of the pommel must be adjusted to allow for efficient lifting and use of the blade. Guard and pommel have to be assembled with a strong and accurate fit. The grip must be shaped in such a way that permits good blade control and secure purchase. The hilt should be made with definite specifications fashioned in a style that is concordant with the era and type of the sword.

To be acceptable, the components of the hilt must reflect the subtle difference in the volume and shape as seen in original hand-crafted components. Wax models that show the dimensions and forms of hand-forged originals can be made to be used as a prototype to be borrowed by manufacturing companies. Instead of handcrafting every original piece—which would be time-consuming and exorbitant, creating an investment casting by using a hand-crafted wax original can be done to achieve the same results.

It is recommended to use the higher priced and more accurate investment casting—also referred to as the 'lost-wax' method—instead of the less expensive and easier sand-casting procedure. Sand casting can be suitable for specific applications, but the intricate details required for the procedure I explain in this section cannot be produced using this technique. Producing the hilt component from a wax original to a complete piece ready for assemblage on a sharp blade requires a lot of efficient working hours.

Step 1:

A prototype for each component is sculpted from a block of solid modeling wax. This process requires extreme care and great effort; thus, sculpting and polishing are done for many hours.

The wax prototype must reflect all the detailing and show the distinctive shape of the prototype. The precise size of the pommel is achieved by testing the original blade for maximum balance in handling and performance. The quantity of the original wax is estimated, creating a space for the type of material used in casting the pommel (steel and bronze possess separate weights) and a contraction in the molding and casting process (roughly 3 – 5%).

Step 2:

The wax prototype must be shaped into two symmetrical halves as soon as it is made. The production or investment waxes will be created using this prototype. It is important that the mold is free of irregularities and long-lasting enough to produce wax each time so that the details would be exactly like the original and would need little to no finishing.

Step 3:

Before adjustments, rough investment waxes are made from production molds. Waxes are poured out into this mold according to a manufacturing schedule; demands for these pieces must already be prepared. Each wax is poured, left to cool and then extricated from the mold. Check the waxes for irregularities or flaws on the surface which are then fixed or condemned. Pouring, checking, and preparing waxes for casting all requires long hours. Condemned waxes can be melted again to enable them to be used again. Every investment created from these molds is used once because the process of investment damages them.

Step 4:

The waxes are 'sprued' before investments; this implies that 'branches' of wax are connected to act as pouring vents or gates (to facilitate the exit of gases from the molten metal)

After 'spruing' the wax, it is dipped in liquid investment solution—a suspension that resembles ceramic (for more intricate pieces, a brush or spray painting is used to pre-paint investment solutions on the wax. The same treatment used for a ceramic or clap pot is also used for this coating—the coating is left to dry and fired in a kiln in an inverted manner to not only harden the ceramic shell but also to 'burn away' the investment wax.

Step 5:

Grind away the large sprues in the hilt components precisely. A first refinishing is done on the total component (because the investment constantly creates a slightly 'gravelly' surface that has to be polished off) and the pieces checked for irregularities. Other detailing that has been lost during the casting process can be regenerated carefully. Some small irregularities are often left deliberately to reproduce the 'character mark' seen on handcrafted hilt component. Following the restoration of all the details, prepare the hilt component for assemblage. Although a few processes like adjusting rough castings are done in sets, every sword assembly is treated individually, not only for craft but also for quality control purposes. The final assemblage is started by mounting one set of casting is on a particular blade.

Step 6:

The guard is brought very close to the base of the blade by hand filing. It is then hammered to fix it firmly on the shoulders of the blade. The hammer is then used to 'peen' the edges of the tang opening on the top of the guard to wedge the sides more tightly against the tang. Check the tight fit of the pommel on this NextGen Baron Next. The pommel is fixed to the end of the tang; this requires additional hand filing of the tang slot before hammering the pommel into position to make sure that it seats tightly in the correct position. After this, the pommel is then hammered to the end of the tang, wedging it firmly into place at the blade end. The end of the tang sticking out of the pommel is then filed into shape in preparation for peening. In some designs, an ornamental rivet block is included as an additional piece (most times, a truncated pyramid shape) that sits in position on top of the pommel.

Step 7:

Depending on the demands of the specific sword models, while cooling, the peen can be hammered flush or into an irregular decorative shape. The pin is then finished with care by being ground flush and polished, or filed into an ornamental block of peen. When a wet block is needed, the tang is 'peened' on top of the end of the wet block, and the peen and net-block are hand-filed to the finishing form.

Note: Because the pommel is permanently wedged into position on the tang, the peen isn't responsible for holding the sword in place. Each component sits without the support of the other.

Step 8:

A custom-made, stabilized birch core is then used to hand-fit the tang. Stabilized wood is used as it is resistant to expansion and contraction from humidity and weather changes and has greater strength and is more long-lasting for heavy use. The model of the sword determines the volume and shape of the core. Once the core is fitted, and epoxy glue is used to fix it into place permanently, risers and other details are added (as in the past) with a cotton cord or linen. The spacing, diameter, and length of cord riders are different and determined by the accuracy demands of that period.

CHAPTER 6. LEATHERWORK FOR KNIVES AND SCABBARD MAKING FOR SWORDS

How to Create a Sheath for a Knife

There are times when you would want an item to be as near as possible— exactly where you need it, not inside your pocket. A sheath can be created for a pocket watch, knife, cell phone, compass, or other objects you don't want to search for. You might like to create something to keep a multi-tool or any tool you want to be close every time. This section is beneficial for the knife you (may have) produced and it also helps you learn leather wet-shaping techniques. Leather can be expanded and molded in the shape of different objects once it is saturated.

Materials and Tools required:

- 5 – 6 ounces of medium-weight leather
- X-ACTO knife or Rotary cutter
- Needles to stitch the leather
- Saran wrap
- Dish towel
- Pencil
- Cardboard from a file folder
- Rowel wheel
- Fid
- Groover tool
- Thread or artificial sinew, already waxed

Steps for Making a Leather Sheath

Step 1. Pattern Drawing

Place your knife on your piece of cardboard; then outline the blade and the extent of the blade you want to be sheathed. The design is not equal because the back of the sheath has an elongation that will be folded eventually and stitched to create a loop that your belt would be threaded through. Note that perfection isn't necessary and it should be preferably oversize than too small.

Step 2. Make a Cut-Out and Assemble Your Pattern

With a pair of scissors, cut roughly to have an idea of the way your pattern would look when the knife is laid out. If this is to your satisfaction, fold the design in half, along the line that would later become the back part of the blade, and cut off the excess material so that the design is well-formed. Press the paper against the blade to know where it is located on the design. After doing this, what you see is a slight wrinkle on the cardboard that shows excess space between the blade and the edges of the cardboard. Then use a little adhesive tape to create the design in the exact three-dimensional shape your leather will be; this permits you to make alterations now when it is easier. Clip off the excess design to level it out and expose the handle a bit more. A few more trimmings and you'll be able to cut out the actual leather sheath. Cut off the tape holding your designs together and make it flat.

Step 3. Tracing and Cutting Your Leather Piece

Draw your pattern on the wrong side of the leather (the furry suede side), this is done because 1. it is not difficult; and 2. it structures the loop of the belt so that the right side faces forward. Usually, I overlook the belt loops section of the loop and only use it as a guide to trace along the piece using a ruler to ensure that it is straight and of adequate length.

Using a rotary cutter, make a cut-out of your leather but be careful so you do not cut into the inside edges where the blade part of the sheath joins the loop because by doing this, you will cut too much and make unattractive dents. Do not touch these areas; use only a sharp knife or an X-ACTO knife to complete the cuts.

Step 4. Begin to Create Leather

Using a lot of plastic wraps, wrap your preferred item (knife, compass, whatever) and tape it in to enfold it in properly. Lay out your dish towel, the item you want to sheath, a pan of hot tap water and the spring clips. Put the sheath part of your leather in hot water; as the leather absorbs the water, the color changes and you see bubbles. A few minutes is enough for this. Position your leather on the dish towel, fold the towel on the leather, and press down to dry it gently and mop off excess water. Position the knife on your leather and fold it over, pressing it along the handle as you progress. Firmly fix the leather into place using the spring clips; manipulate the leather, so it takes the shape of the blade handle. You can press the leather with your fingers to firmly attach it to the handle. Allow to dry. Though, check every five minutes for the first 30 minutes to ensure that the leather is molded to your satisfaction. Your leather can be used after several hours depending on the humidity and temperature, or you can choose to let it stay through the night. Remove the spring clips as soon as the leather is dry, and this would create a sheath 'husk.'

Step 5. Sheath Trimming and Preparing to Stitch the Seam

Trim the sheath to its actual size by cutting off the rough edges while following the outline of the blade and handle; to do this, use a rotary cutter. Since you are cutting through two layers of leather that are already hardened by water, you will need to apply more pressure. Do this carefully, so you do not cut yourself. Cut a shallow groove into the leather using the edge of the sheath seam as a guide, use a leather gouge to do this. It can also be done freehand or with a gouge that has an inbuilt guide. Using a rowel tool, mark your stitches in the groove. Six holes in every inch are enough. In the absence of a rowel tool, it can be done freehand, but this requires utmost care and precision. Position your sheath on a plastic cutting board and use your fid to make holes in the depression already made with the rowel tool. Tap your fid lightly with a small mallet. Once all the holes have been filled, pull up the top layer of the sheath and do the same for your bottom because your fid will have holes on the bottom layer as well. Ensure that they are properly aligned or your stitching would be stressful; in the absence of a fid, an ice pick, or any pointed object can be used. Fids are preferable because they create small slits and not holes.

Step 6. Sew up the Belt Loop

It is better to sew the belt loop now before stitching the sheath up. Fold your belt flap over to the front and correct it to your preferred size before trimming. It should fasten immediately below the top of the sheath. Once it is too deep, it may be difficult for the handle to properly seat in the sheath.

With the use of a four-prong punch, create an arrow of holes in the belt end of the loop and the top of the sheath. A fid, ice pick, or any sharp and pointy object can be used if you do not have a four-prong punch. If there is excess leather, trim it away from the end of the strap. Use your needle and artificial sinew to stitch the loop, going inward and outward until the stitches are visible. Tie your thread off and get your sinew cut close to the knot.

Step 7. Sewing the Seam

Use a sinew and a single needle to begin sewing from the lower part of the piece, close to the upper part of the sheath. Make a stitch with the side moving up through the leather and down into the next hole. A double-needle technique could be used, but since the seam is short, a single-needle technique will do. Once you have gotten to the end of your sheath, turn around and move up starting from the bottom, doing the reverse of what you just did. The effect is to make it tight enough to prevent it from loosing; the thread is protected with the groove in the leather and properly aligned with the leather or below the surface of the leather. Tie off the knots and thread the needle a few times inward and outward. Complete by threading the needle through a single layer of leather and draw taut. Cut off the lacing flush together with the seam to hide it. Use the wooden end of your fid to polish the seam of your sheath to even out the stitches then press it downwards into the sheath.

Step 8. Slide Your Knife In

Slide in your knife. It should be a little tight; it will loosen after a while. Position it on your belt. Take pleasure in the fact that you created something nice.

Sword Scabbard

Throughout history, scabbards were created (from middle, outward) from wood, leather, or wool. Then, two thin planks are also soaked and curved to take the shape of the blade. This is more time consuming, and with the tools I use, I would create a 'wedged' scabbard—two plain ones and one with a groove.

The materials and tools required are:

- Sword—Obviously, but not necessary. Every scabbard is customized, and the size is determined by the sword. If it isn't customized, it may not fit (sword might easily slip off and fall) or too snug (like the Excalibur-style scabbard) and can't be brought out once inserted.

- Wooden plank—The smallest size that can be used: blade length +5 – 10 cm, width of blade 4 cm. Adding excess length makes your scabbard more pointed. Make sure to select a plank that has the exact thickness of your blade or a bit less.
- Leather—has to be a lot bigger than the wood plank because you will almost certainly cut your leather badly. The leather is also needed for the pattern and covering the pattern. I suggest that you buy leftover leather instead, as it is very affordable. You might want to buy leather laces to use it in strapping the bridge for instance.
- Wood piece for the bridge—size is determined by what you want
- Plenty of clamps
- Wood glue and brush
- Already waxed thread and leather needles.
- Leather glue (wood glue can be used if you want)
- Wood oil and finish—Select oil that is resistant to humidity and torsion, like outdoor furniture oil and wood flooring waxed oil. I had a leftover of flooring transparent wax oil, which worked fine. Clean the brush with petrol—better for oil brushes
- Special leather thread as the typical sewing thread isn't strong enough.
- Elastics
- Soap
- Ladder
- Pen
- 220-paper sander
- Jigsaw
- Mask and goggles
- Belt sander
- Tissue paper
- Leather hole punch
- Expandable towel
- Leather cutter
- Cutter mat
- Dremel
- Two buckets

Steps for Making a Scabbard
Step 1. Construct the Bridge

Although this step is not obligatory as a FIRST step, it MUST be carried out before Step 5. Draw a pattern out to have on it some three-dimensional relief–to ensure that you will be able to place the lace pattern on the appropriate place, think of lacing and belt.

- To start with, draw out the holes you will like to have.
- You see its side on the schema.

- At least, you need a bottom hole that is big (to enable you to pass the strap that is used to tie the belt)—double holes on its upper part enables you to pass the laces and to tie it up on the scabbard.
- The double holes on the bottom side are not important. Create them in a way to get the lace on the scabbard surrounded; it can be solely flat.
- To cut off those holes, make use of whatever you want. A jigsaw could be used. A scroll saw is the best option if you have it.
- After you have done that, utilize the Dremel and belt sander to round the entire thing.
- Utilize mask and goggles
- You may have the desire to draw some art on it. I carved using a dremel. Also, you may pyro-draw; or do nothing, plain wood is okay as well.
- After that is done, consider treating the wood (oiling, varnishing, or anything else) and allow it to dry.

Step 2. Measure, Trace and Cut the Planks

- Place your sword on top of the plank, your traces ought to be 2 cm bigger than the width of the blade (1 cm on each of its side), and it should be 5 – 10 cm longer in length than the original length (this is dependent on how pointy you need the scabbard to be).
- Trace three nice rectangles out of those measured above (rectangles ought to be similar).
- Right at each rectangle's center, place the blade nicely (utilize the ladder to put the point accurately, a length of 1 cm on each of the guard's side), and draw out the profile of the blade. After this, fill the profile (to enable you to see where the blade is meant to be with less difficulty).
- Repeat these six times—three rectangles, two faces on every rectangle.
- Cut up the three rectangles.
- You will be required to cut the internal portion on one of the rectangles (the part where the blade goes). Because the sides are thin, they can disintegrate easily, so you have to be extremely careful (when using a jigsaw especially).
- It is okay if it breaks once or twice. You don't need to do it again (I would though, as a perfectionist), the issue might be fixed by gluing it all together.
- I just utilized a wood driller (25 mm) to cut the tip out to make a decent curve.

Step 3. Tryouts, Inner Scrape, and Glue Planks

Now is the time to be sure it fits your sword perfectly.

- You don't want it to be too loose or too tight, do not forget this. Clamp your three planks together (hole plank at the center) just like a sandwich without using any glue. Perfectly align them (and utilize the blade markup on the planks). Utilize plenty of clamps; the wood has to be very tight together so you should simulate the gluing.
- Make attempts to put in the blade.
- You will need to add something on the plain planks to add some thickness if it's excessively loose (it just keeps sliding in and off by gravity) Fabrics would be okay. Wool fabrics are even better.

- You will need to scrape a little of the plain planks to include some space in case it's excessively tight (you may have to push a bit though). Make use of a Dremel for that purpose—to make its internal portion smooth and to prevent damage to the blade, utilize the 220 sandpaper after that.
- Continue to repeat the process until it becomes tight enough. It will be a bit more tightened by gluing it together, so it must be a bit, just a little bit, not enough to tighten it to your taste.
- To clean the planks, a wet tissue could be used for this and take away all of the wood junk gotten as a result of this procedure.
- To get the planks glued together, you need to have the glue on the whole side, so you should use a brush.
- Glue one plank that is plain to the hole plank, clamp it together, use a tissue to clean the exceeding glue that is inside (to prevent making thickness with glue) and wait for 30 minutes till it's dry enough.
- Glue the last of the planks to the assembly and clamp it together. To be certain that the exceeding glue is not creating thickness, slide your blade in and out for about 3 – 5 times. After this, CLEAN UP YOUR BLADE!!! (WD40, gun oil, and so on)
- Wait till the glue is dry (read recommendations from the manufacturer of the glue)

Step 4. Outer Scrape & Oil Wood Scabbard

- On the table, fix your belt Sander and start scraping it to have an oval that is nice. You don't want to end up with any hole on the blade space, so TAKE AS MUCH TIME AS YOU NEED.
- Use goggles and mask
- Oil its outer part (add a great amount of oil, as much as possible, it ought to get into the wood's thickness).
- Allow it to dry up (read up recommendations from the manufacturer of the oil).

Step 5. Draw a Pattern to Have Some 3D Relief on It–Think About Belt and Lacing

- To draw out the pattern, use a leather strap of length 5 mm, they are directly glued on to the wood.
- At the barest minimum, to make two gaps to bind the bridge you will need to have four straps.
- A bigger spacer should be added a little more in the center, to have the strap which will be in charge of maintaining the sword diagonally on your hip.
- Then just for the outward appearance, add some pattern.

Step 6. Cut and Punch Holes on to the Covering Leather

- Cut up the covering leather. Cutting it up is tricky, the issue is that you don't want to have excessive leather, neither do you want to have it insufficient
- On each of the sides, punch holes evenly on them

Step 7. Prepare Covering Pattern

- You should set up a covering pattern. This is to be applied on the leather (step 9) once it's all sewed up and it is drying; this is done to have a nice 3D relief as the outcome.
- Consider your leather's thickness; it ought not to touch the glued pattern exactly, add a gap of +-2 mm (depending on the thickness of your covering leather).

Step 8. Soak Leather & Prepare Sewing & Gluing

- Make provisions for a basin of cold-ish water—present temperature
- Prepare another basin of water that has been heated (not boiling water; something like a temperature between 40 and 60 degrees).
- For the entire leather soaking and molding process, if you want to know more about it, refer to Google. This procedure was flawless to me; it gave adequate time to sew and fix pattern before it's too hard, the leather was still soft enough after that (no need for it to be solid leather), etc.
- Soak up your piece of leather in cold water for ten minutes.
- Make provisions for a long waxed thread (it should be approx. 4 – 5 times your scabbard's length) and two different needles during those ten minutes. In case you end up with a thread that is excessively short (or you need it to be shorter to ease its sewing).
- You can cover up your scabbard of glue, once you are done with this. Make use of a brush to apply glue on all the wood.
- Once the preparation is done, the leather should have been soaked for approximately ten minutes now. Change your buckets, soak the leather inside water that is mildly warm for a period of 1 – 2 minutes (not more than this, the warmer the water is, the lesser the soaking time ought to be) and go on to the NEXT STEP (quickly).

Step 9. Sew, Apply Your Covering Pattern, and Allow it to Dry Overnight

- Pick up your leather piece, dry it up a little on your towel (its internal part, to prevent the dripping of water like hell on the wood) place it on your towel, outside and facing downwards on a table, place the scabbard on it and begin to sew.
- You should try to be fast (however, you should not be too fast, don't make errors) and, also preferably, on your sewing as well (if the diagonal, top left down to the bottom right is on the upper side on the first cross, it ought to be so all the time. Use blue thread on the external site).
- You should tighten it well, however, be careful not to break the leather. You should not hesitate to apply the leather very well with your hands, and if you must, stretch it.
- To prevent having problems with the thread, endeavor not to touch the glue too much with the needle or thread.
- NEVER USE YOUR FINGERNAILS, it will only leave bad traces.
- To stop the wire when you get to the throat, turn three crosses downward.
- You may now apply the covering pattern (to upgrade 3D relief & shape the leather) and tightly wrap it using elastics or cord, probably some clamps here and there. Allow it to dry overnight.

ADVANCED GUIDE TO BLADESMITHING

- Take off the covering wrapping & pattern in the morning and enjoy.

Step 10. Finish Throat and Chape (Leather Finish)

- As regards the throat, to enable the leather finishes to stay directly upon the guard, cut off the exceeding leather to leave a length of approx. 2 mm on both sides (thickness of the wood's edges). After this, add some glue and then paste the leather on it. To enable you to apply some pressure to keep it glued, slide in the sword so that the guard would create some pressure.
- As for the chape (the scabbard's ending), opt for one made of leather (or of metal). Just sew two portions together, soak it up for ten minutes, after this soak it in water that is VERY HOT (almost boiling) for two minutes (to make the leather hard). After this, apply it on the tip and allow it to dry overnight.

Step 11. Strap the Bridge, Belt or Baldric

To start with, you will lace the bridge on top of the scabbard, right on the placements which you have rendered before covering. Make sure that the lace is excessively tight; the bridge holds the straps that carry the entire assembly (sword and scabbard).

CHAPTER 7. GRIP MATERIALS AND SCRIMSHAW

Just as the knife blades are important, Knife handles are also important. The knife will fail to function appropriately in the absence of a good handle. Due to the knife handle's importance, I have provided this information about the common styles and kinds of knife handles that exist. Handles of knives have been created out of pretty much every kind of material imaginable, ranging from the weird materials to incredibly nice looking and practical materials. Today, there are many artificial and natural materials that are nice for the creation of knife handles.

Grip Materials

The major purpose of the list below is to offer you some idea of the more common kinds of knife handle materials that are used in present times. You may likewise enjoy a list that is more detailed.

Abalone. This is a natural material obtained from a mollusk's shell. It is harvested off the coast of California, Mexico, and other regions of the South Pacific. Although it possesses an appearance that is extremely satisfying, it is not so durable compared to some other materials used for making knife handle. Its most widely known to be used as gentleman's pocket knives, here it will not experience exposure to the tumble and roughness outdoor use of a heavy-duty knife. Also, an imitation abalone is produced from a kind of plastic which is majorly used for the handle of pocket knives.

ABS. This is a black amorphous thermoplastic terpolymer, which possesses the strength of high impact. Resistance and toughness which are incredible characteristics for knife handles are the most astounding mechanical properties ABS possesses. Mostly, it is used for everyday working knives.

African Blackwood. An African Blackwood, also referred to as Mozambique Ebony, this is a rich black with dark brown graining. It is one of the extremely best woods for making handles of knives; it is used to produce fine clarinets.

Almite. This is a coating used on handles made from aluminum, like anodizing. It has resistance to scratching and marring. Also, it can be tinted to any color of your choice for it to be visually appealing.

Aluminum. Aluminum is a non-ferrous metal just like titanium is. It is commonly used as knife handles; aluminum provides the knife with a solid feel with the additional weight absent. Aluminum provides a solid feel for the knife's handle with the extra weight absent, and it is also very durable. It can be made to offer a grasp that is secure and comfortable. The T6-6061, a heat-treatable grade is the most common aluminum form. Anodizing is the most common finishing procedure for aluminum, and it adds color and protection to the handle.

Amber. This is a fossilized pitch from pre-historic evergreens, greatly utilized in jewelry; presently used by a few producers of handmade knives.

Ambidextrous. It is used with both hands with no difficulty. It is a knife which has not been exclusively created for a left- or right-handed individual but can be used with an equal amount of ease by the two hands.

Amboina Wood (spelled as Amboyna as well). Sometimes it is called padouk; it is an uncommon, exotic hardwood with a fragrant smell varying in color from red color to golden brown to yellow. It is utilized in cabinet production, and it is an incredible wood choice for both turning and finishing. It is obtained from the *Pterocarpus indicus* tree of the Southeast Asia jungles.

Anodized Aluminum. This is subjecting aluminum to electrolytic activity, which coats the aluminum with a film that is defensive and decorative.

Axis Deer (India Stag). The smaller sized of the SE Asian deer and the two Indian that provide antler for the knife production industry; all these are shed horn collected by the natives inside the jungle.

Bi-Directional Texturing. This is Spyderco's patented texture design molded into FRN handles with forward and backward graduating steps emanating outward from the handle's center. It gives resistance to slipping off from the hand.

Black Mother of Pearl. In today's knife market, this is one of the most sought-after exclusive pearls. It is obtained from small shells discovered in French Polynesia around Tahiti. Just beneath the exterior bark of the shell, there lies the Blacklip shell's real magnificence. From the standpoint of durability and utilization, it is extremely like abalone.

Bone. The bone which is utilized to make handles of knives is obtained from animals that died naturally. For improved grip and additional beauty, handles of bone are usually given a surface texture. To create the surface texture on the bone, jigging is the most widely recognized approach, and it is carried out utilizing a special machine for jigging in which modified bits cut out bone pieces. The machine works in a rocking motion to deliver the specific pattern that is wanted. Every one of the patterns possesses its distinguished look. The bone can be dyed in an assortment of colors after it has been jigged. Owing to the facts that bone is durable, fairly less difficult to shape and can be attractive, it is a very great material for knife handles. It is one of the most well-known handle material utilized for pocket knives.

Carbon Fiber. Fibers of Graphite (human hair sizes) are woven together and fused inside the epoxy resin. It possesses lightweight; it is three-dimensional in appearance and is a superior (and costly) handle material. It has a profound futuristic look with a definite "ahhhhh" factor. It is likely that Carbon fiber is the strongest of all the lightweight manufactured handle materials. The carbon strand's ability to reflect light, making the pattern of the weave extremely visible is the main visual attraction this material possesses. Additionally, carbon fiber is a labor-intensive material that produces a knife that is rather expensive.

Chital (check Axis – India Stag). The smaller of both the Indian and SE Asian deer that furnish antler for the knife business; all these are shed horn collected in the jungle by locals.

Cocobolo Wood. Hardwood obtained from the Cocobolo tree, and it ranges in color from dark purple to deep red and bright orange. The wood's grain and fine texture are relatively not difficult to work, shines to a high sheen and is well known as an inlay or embellishment on handles of knives.

Cordia Wood. This wood type is extremely similar to Teak, and occasionally, it is utilized as a substitute for Teak when it comes to building ships.

Desert Ironwood. This wood is native to the Sonoran desert in southern Arizona and Northern Sonora Mexico. The wood is exceptionally dense and tight grained, it takes an extremely high polish, and tends to darken with use and age.

European Stag. Antler obtained from the Red Deer, a big elk-like creature found all around Europe. For at least as long as knives of metal have existed, and likely a long time before then, it has been utilized to make handles of knives. Never has this stag been a substitute for the axis and sambar deer of Southeast Asia and India's antlers. Much like the American elk, the European Red Deer's center is exceptionally coarse and open. Mostly, it has to be utilized as handle scales due to the expansive measure of pith in the center. The Red Deer's antler is a limited substitute for both the Axis and the Sambar's antlers.

Fiberglass Reinforced Nylon. A nylon polymer combined with glass fiber which is then injected into a mold to create lightweight handles of knives.

Forprene. Forprene is a material that is highly resistant, an elastopolymer with extremely high thermal properties from a temperature of -40 Degrees C to +150 degrees C; it has exceptional high-grip power. Also, the material is exceptionally salt and acid corrosion- resistant and can be utilized in every single wet situation.

G-10. G-10 is a laminate that is fiberglass based. Layers of fiberglass cloth are soaked inside resin, compressed and then baked after this. The resulting material is hard, lightweight, and solid. The surface texture is included in checkering form or other patterns. Because it is durable and lightweight as well, it is a perfect material for tactical folders and fixed blades of knives. It comes in different colors.

Glass Filled Nylon. A great number of today's thermoplastic materials are improved on by adding chopped glass strands. Regularly, as much as 40% of a product's percentage might be glass. It adds incredible strength.

German Silver. It is a combination of copper, zinc, and nickel. It is otherwise referred to as Nickel Silver.

Jigged Bone. Obtained from dead animals, mostly a cow's chin bone. Generally, the bone is dyed, and by cutting grooves into the bone, surface texture is acquired. It was first utilized in the imitation of genuine stag scales.

Kraton. This is a thermoplastic polymer which is rubbery and is utilized for the handle of knives or as a flexible inlay on knife handles for an improved grip.

Laminated Handles are handles created from different materials that are layered together and held together by glue.

Leather. On some hunting and military knives, leather handles are present. By stacking leather washers or as a sleeve encompassing another handle material, leather handles are typically created. Although knife handles made of leather are attractive to look at, they are not as durable as some other materials. As spacers to add accents to the handle of a knife, leather functions admirably.

Mammoth Bone (Molar and Ivory as well). Rarely utilized in custom knives. It is found during mining tasks in the far north, in locations with plenty of glacial activity. The distinguishable look is created from erosion.

Micarta. When it comes to construction, Micarta is similar to G-10. Either canvas, linen cloths, or paper layers are soaked inside a phenolic resin. Pressure and heat are applied to the layers which ignite a chemical response (polymerization) to occur. The final product is a material that is lightweight and strong. Because of its extraordinary toughness and stability, Micarta is a well-known handle material on user knives. Micarta has come to be known as practically any fibrous material placed in resin. It's available in an assortment of colors and laminate materials. Micarta is very smooth to touch; it does not possess surface texture. This material demands hand labor, which implies a higher valued knife. If not treated appropriately, Micarta is a material that is relatively soft and can be scratched.

Mother of Pearl. The pearl oyster's shell from the South Pacific; a knife handle material that is costly and well known.

Natural Materials. Natural materials, for instance, jigged bone, mother of pearl, abalone, leather, stabilized woods and stone that are utilized in creating and embellishing handles.

Palmira Wood. Kitul Black Palmira possess a unique structure with dark, nearly black, tough streaks in a background matrix that is paler. Although it is hard to work, it produces results that are very dramatic.

Pearl. The pearl oyster's shell from the South Pacific; a costly and well-known knife handle material.

Peel Ply Carbon Fiber. It is a carbon fiber filled, epoxy resin lay-up that has textured material set superficially to protect the material while manufacturing is going on. The material is removed after production, and it leaves a texture that is grippy in the epoxy creating a non-slip handle material.

Polycarbonate. A strong synthetic resin utilized in molded items, for instance, handles of knives, unbreakable windows, and optical lenses.

Sambar. An extremely large, elk-sized deer found in India and S.E. Asia; the antler is utilized for knife handles and is referred to as or India stag.

Sermollan. A plastic that is rubberized and utilized on kitchen knife handles. It offers a secure grasp and is resistant to bacteria.

Stag. Stag is also another material that is very popular. Because of its high density when compared to others, Sambar Stag antler material is the most sought after for creating knife handles of all the species of deer. Most Sambar Stag is from India and due to the ban by the government on its export, it is becoming increasingly expensive and uncommon. Stag is obtained from naturally shed deer antlers. Stag takes on that slightly burnt look when exposed to open fire. Sambar Stag makes superb knife handle material, and it's extremely durable.

Stainless Steel. Is referred to as steel that contains at least 12-1/2-13% chromium, making it corrosion-resistant (it is not stain-proof). The chromium oxide CrO prevents the formation of rust by creating a barrier to oxygen and moisture. Although various grades of stainless steel exist, nearly all stainless steel blades contain a great amount of high carbon, so none are entirely "stainless." All grades are liable to corrosion from humidity, body acid, salt, etc. The term has come to imply that the steel has a fewer amount of carbon and more amount of chromium, and will, therefore, stainless than the majority of other steels. To make it less difficult to grip, it is regularly utilized in combination with a different material such as rubber or plastic. The weight is the greatest drawback to the handle of stainless steel knives.

Titanium. Titanium is a metal that is known to be harder but lighter when compared to steel. While stainless steel handled knives are more often than not on the heavy side, titanium gives the toughness and durability of a metal handle that does not have so much weight. Of any steel, Titanium provides the most resistance to corrosion. It possesses a decent "feel" and makes a fantastic material for knife handles.

Valox. A handle material obtained from reinforced resin.

Volcano Grip. This term is Spyderco's trademark for the waffle texture found in their fiberglass reinforced nylon handled lightweight knives. While cutting, the continuous pattern of small-sized squares offers a better hand grasp.

White Mother of Pearl. A highly valued knife handle material! It originates from the silver lip shell. Few of the best White Mother of Pearl originates from tropical Australia's South Seas. It is extremely uncommon in sizes large enough to utilize for knife scales. It is known that 10 tons of pearl shells are required to obtain material large enough to cut sizes 1/10" x 4-1/2" long. From the angle of durability and advantages, it is also highly similar to abalone.

Wood. Wood handles of knives vary from the more typical wood species to the most exotic species, and the value ranges accordingly. For hunting knives or for uses that involve a great deal of moisture or water, soft or fine woods such as black walnut are bad choices. Hardwoods such as Rosewood, oak, and maple are good choices for making hunting knives. Stabilized wood such as mesquite, desert ironwood, and spalted maple are available where the wood is infused with plastic making it waterproof and furnishing it with a durable finish which does not need any maintenance apart from buffing it occasionally. For tough duty knives and knives that would come in contact with a great deal of moisture, these are highly recommended. Exotic and Fancy knives with wood handles are particularly popular with collectors. A wood handle that is of good quality will be durable and can be attractive, too.

Wood Epoxy Laminate. It is an impregnated wood laminate, which is very hard and machines in a way that is similar to Corian, aluminum, and Micarta.

Zytel. This thermoplastic material was developed by Du Pont. ZYTEL is the most economical to create of all synthetic materials. It cannot be broken: it resists effect and abrasions. ZYTEL possess a slight texture in regards to its surface, but knife companies utilizing this material will include extra, aggressive surface texture to in addition to the slight texture it possesses. For utilizing Zytel, SOG Specialty Knives is not rare.

Numerous other materials utilized for making handles of knives exist as well as different kinds of plastics and exotic materials for instance: warthog tusks, mammoth tooth, and ivory, oosic (walrus penis bone), stone, sheep and buffalo horn, etc. Practically all hard material can be (and has been) utilized as a knife handle.

How to Scrimshaw

Scrimshaw is a classic American folk art form that was once perfected by sailors from New England. They would make designs onto whale ivory using needles or knives and color it using ink or soot. Although the whaling trade is not viable or legitimate anymore, the scrimshaw craft lives on.

Part 1. Finding Materials to use

1. Check ancient salvage yards or thrift stores for small sized ivory pieces. If you are utilizing whale ivory, ensure that it was harvested before the year 1972 when the Marine Protection Act banned whaling in America. You can likewise utilize ancient keys of an ivory piano, bone or white acrylic.
2. Purchase a pen-like X-ACTO knife that has a replaceable head. Introduce a pin into the front and secure this pinhead inside the knife.
3. Obtain some beeswax, black, brown or blue ink and some acetone nail polish cleaner, all of good quality.

PART 2. Sealing the surface

1. Rub beeswax to the uppermost of the ivory or bone to seal it, if you can, put a disk to a Dremel tool and rub the beeswax on the disc, too. Again, rub the beeswax equally to the topmost area of the ivory, covering it. Why are we sealing the ivory if you may ask? This is done because ivory is penetrable. This sealing will help keep the ink that is tattooed into the ivory away from dropping over into where it isn't needed, leaving an inky cloud. If you properly sealed, the ivory will take up only the ink that went into the grooves that were etched into it.
2. Use a dry cloth to spread the beeswax into the surface by hand for like 5 minutes especially if you do not have the needed tool to work with, try to apply the beeswax all over the ivory evenly until it gets to all part of it
3. Using a clean cloth next, polish the ivory until all the beeswax has been taken off. The ivory should be very sparkling at this point but no longer glistening, keep the beeswax cloth aside since you will still need it later

Part 3. Transferring a design

1. Measure your piece of ivory; you will need to use your scrimshaw as your small detailed drawing
2. Look for an image online and resize to the size of your object, ensure to leave one-half inch of space on all sides. A really good draft out image will perfect outlines, and maybe some shadowing will be helpful with scrimshaw.
3. Either you print the image using a computer, or you copy it from a book to a white paper.
4. You can now place the ivory on top of it and draw an online of the ivory over the white paper, or you cut it to straighten it with the edges swiftly.
5. Now place the illustration face down on the paper, dampened a clean cloth with acetone nail remover and apply it gently over the top of the paper using the cloth and then again with a bone folder. Ensure that the paper is moist.

6. You can now lift the edge of the paper and remove it back very fast. Don't try moving it around on the exterior to avoid smudging your outline. You can throw away the paper now. Check it out if the edge didn't come off on the bone visibly, then try to sand it, maybe wax it and redo it.

Part 4. Etching the surface

1. Use your pen to draw the outlines of the illustration, start by applying pressure withholding the pin vertically as you can. Etch the lines into the surface of the bone.
2. Complete the outline of the illustration, next, rub some ink on the surface with a cotton swab, rub a good quantity and then clean it off the excess with a lint-free rag
3. Start shading the drawing by etching crosshatched lines. Also, you can stipple by etching dots because the closer the dots to each other, the darker the shading will become.
4. Spread more ink on the cotton swabs and clean it off, note if you need a darker line still, you can draw it deeper and pour more ink on it.
5. Replace your pins if need be when once you noticed it begins to dull

Part 5. Finishing the scrimshaw

1. Recheck your work to identify a mistake immediately if any, then draw larger lines or you sand the area, you can also re-wax or sketch if the mistake needs any of these.
2. Clean all the extra ink away from the surface of the bone
3. Get your beeswax covered cloth, then polish the surface of your scrimshaw when completed by spreading an equal layer over the artwork. This should be sparkling and save the ink.

CHAPTER 8. HEAT TREATING THE BLADE

A good knife will never dull with little use or break with little pressure, but the same can't be said about a bad knife. A good knife will remain sharp for a long while and remain straight and true even with a whole lot of stress on it. This to a large extent is the difference between knife sold in Walmart and a custom handmade knife. With various heating and cooling, steel changes physical properties, your target is to manage these properties to suit the use of a knife. Though you might have heard about this before now, it's also good to get a good knowledge about it proper workings.

The Two Physical Properties

When it comes to knives, there are two needed properties. The first one is a knife hardness and brittleness. A hard knife is likely not to dull, it is also likely to be used a lot on various materials, and the cutting edge will remain solid. Well, a hard can snap easily though. Primarily, the atoms are formed in a rigid pattern; the atoms would rather break bonds than completely move slightly in addition to one another.

The second property a knife should possess is toughness and softness. A good tough knife can be used even when hunting, and it will remain the same. The only problem will be the cutting edge not staying sharp for too long because of its softness and of course it will become a piece of metal that stays in a wedge shape. But on the molecular level, instead of the atoms breaking bonds totally, they would move slightly about each other, this is to say that the cutting edge microscopically folds over itself. This can be seen as a sliding scale, one end is hard, and at the other end, it feels tough. Your target should be to get the right stability of the two as hard as you can and also make it remain sharp as long as you can. But you should still be careful not to make it too hard that it will get easily broken under some reasonable pressure. It should be able to stay for a long time. Going to the actual process the step by step heat treating will be discussed, and a molecular explanation will be given as well. It will be great to know the science behind this so that it will help in resolving issues if you ever run into any of them

Equipment and Materials:

- Tongs or visegrip pliers
- Forge
- Oven
- Fireproof quench container and cover
- Quenching medium like motor oil
- Fire extinguisher that puts out oil and grease fires
- Heat resistant gloves and face shield
- Fireproof material for regulator block such as an aluminum tube
- One forged or stock removed high or mild carbon steel knife blank

Heat Treatment and Etching Process of Damascus

Materials needed: 1095 and 15N20

Process

1. Heat the blade to between 760 and 790 degrees C meaning critical temperature
2. Quench in light or quenching oil
3. Lastly, drag temper to a possible hardness

Heating

The blade should be gently and evenly heated to a bright red or dull orange color about 760 to 815 degree C should be used, this likes heating up to about 15-20 minutes. Ensure you do not overheat it as an overheated blade can become cracked or warped when quenched.

Hold at the critical temperature for up to 3 minutes. You can as well try this other good method, of heating the blade till it loses all its magnetic properties. This usually happens at about 770 degrees C. If you, therefore, want to ascertain that a blade is ready for use, you can quench it with a magnet. When there is little attraction or none at all between the magnet and the blade, be sure that the ideal temperature has been reached and is ready to quench.

Quenching

Quenching can conveniently be done in either the standard quenching oil or in light oil. Oil quench can be used on a large blade where toughness is needed more while brine quench is needed more on a smaller folder and skinner blades where holding an edge is very important. Brine quenching can be used for smaller blades too. This will help make the blade be very hard as it will assist in cooling the steel much quicker than even the oil. But you have to be careful when quenching in brine. There is a higher likelihood of the blade cracking if it's cooled immediately. The best bet is to preheat the brine to about 100 degrees before quenching. Dissolving salt in boiling water until it no longer melts makes a brine solution. The thin blade needs to be quenched either point first or its spine first, this is to help reduce the opportunity of cracking or warping. To quench the thick blades then the cutting edge should be quenched. First, this will assist in ensuring hardness on the cutting edge and don't forget to keep the blade moving while quenching.

Tempering

Tempering the blade is all about heating the steel in a heat treatment oven. This should be done immediately after quenching to reduce the opportunity of cracking which could stem from remaining stresses. Leave to remain at that temperature to ascertain an even full heat. The excellent way to get the same temper is to heat a bigger size of slab or block of steel to a specific temperature, and then set the blade on that and leaving it there to absorb the heat. Leave it at the tempering temperature as long as you can maintain it or maybe up to an hour. If you had used a large tempering block, then let it be so that the blade will cool together with it. The relative hardness of the blade is dependent on the specific temperature. The recommended drawing timeline should be two hours. Don't forget to leave enough space for each blade to aid proper air circulation.

Deg C	As Quenched	205	260	315
Hardness (RC)	63-65	58-59	56-57	53-54

Heat treatment for stainless steel

Stainless steel is primarily divided into four groups to know their reaction to heat treatments. The precipitation hardening grades, assigned a PH suffix e. g 15-5 PH consists of a group which like the other three achieve both high strength and corrosion resistance. The following is the short notes of the heat treatment potential of the two groups

Ferritic stainless steels: this stainless isn't hardened by quenching. The heat treatment used for ferritic is annealing since they have minimum hardness and maximum flexibility, impact, toughness, and corrosion. Annealing helps to reduce stresses which were generated during the welding or cold working. It helps to provide a better uniform microstructure.

Austenitic stainless steels

The normal austenitic stainless steels will be hard when working with cold but can't be the same when working with heat treatment. Annealing is used to optimize softness, corrosion resistance, and ductility. Nevertheless, post-annealing can be specified after thermal processing or welding. This group is usually bought in the cold worked or annealed condition.

Martensitic stainless steels

The greatest hardness one can achieve when using martensitic stainless steels depends on the carbon content. So, therefore, heat treating this group is the same as for carbon or low alloy steels. The process parameters are different though since the higher alloy content of the group makes them react more slowly. They sometimes show absolute hardenability so that the highest hardness is achieved in the center of the sections which will be up to 30mm that is about 12 inches thick by cool airing. Conclusively, there are two main types of heat treatment.

Annealing helps to lessen hardness and enhance flexibility. Going full annealing is quite costly and take up time too, so it should only be specified when needed for severe forming. Austenitizing quenching and tempering are used to enhance strength and hardness. These methods also affect corrosion resistance; sometimes it needs balancing the heat treatment parameter to optimize corrosion resistance and product strength requirements.

Precipitation hardening

Stainless steels are the most basic forged grades of **precipitation hardening** (PH), stainless steels are a 17-7 PH and 15-5 PH. These grades come together to form high corrosion resistance of austenitic grades with the energy attainable in martensitic grades. There are available procedures for homogenization, austenite conditioning, transformation, cooling and precipitation hardening.

Duplex stainless steels: this is the main forging grades which contain the mixture of both ferrite and austenite in their microstructures. They are always not heat treated other than annealing.

LEAVE A REVIEW?

Throughout the process of writing this book, I have tried to put down as much value and knowledge for the reader as possible. Some things I knew and practice, some others I spent time to research. I hope you found this book to be of benefit to you!

If you liked the book, would you consider leaving a quick review for it? I would be grateful to you for letting other people know that you like it.

Yours Sincerely,

Wes Sander

CONCLUSION: TIME TO STEP UP

While there are a lot of books on bladesmithing, there are only a few books on in-depth knowledge of bladesmithing. With the level of renewed interest in knife and sword making, this book revealed all a blade enthusiast needs to take their learning to the next level. Having known all about the advanced methods of bladesmithing, it's time to step up from being a beginner. You have all you want now. This book contains knowledge you cannot get anywhere.

Bonus: I have 3 **FREE bonuses** for you (check the front of the book for the full description). All you have to do is go to ***http://www.elitebladesmithingmasterclass.com/free-bonus*** and enter the e-mail where you want to receive them.

CPSIA information can be obtained
at www.ICGtesting.com
Printed in the USA
BVHW010854250620
582306BV00015B/133